HOMEOKINETICS:

THE BASICS

Books by Arthur S. Iberall

Foundations for Social and Biological Evolution

On Nature, life, mind, society

Bridges in Science - From Physics to Social Science

Physics of Membrane Transport

On Pulsatile and Steady Arterial Flow - The GTS Contribution

Toward A General Science of Viable Systems

HOMEOKINETICS:
THE BASICS

Arthur S. Iberall

Strong Voices Publishing

Medfield, MA

Strong Voices Publishing
Technical Division
P.O. Box 731
Medfield, MA 02052
www.strongvoicespublishing.com

Reprint of "Homeokinetics: A Physical Science for
Complex Systems" from *Science*, 18 August, 1978, Volume
201, Number 4356, pp. 579-582. Used by permission.

For inquiries, contact info@strongvoicespublishing.com

For more on homeokinetics, go to
www.homeokinetics.org

ISBN-13: 978-0-9905361-4-7
Library of Congress Control Number: 2016912031

"To investigate the essential
attributes of one class of things,
starting from one set of beliefs, is
the business of one science."
    – *Aristotle (384-322 BC)*

"How does homeokinetics
operate to identify form and
function, system and process –
in classic Greek terms, the being
now from the becoming before
and after?"
    – *Arthur S. Iberall (1918-2002)*

DEDICATION

My late father Arthur S. Iberall lived life studying how things worked. With a background in mechanical engineering and theoretical physics, he, with his dear friend Harry Soodak, were able to turn keen observations and insights into a new field of the physics of complex systems. They called it homeokinetics — from the Greek: ὅμοιος *hómoios* meaning "similar" and κίνησις *kinesis* meaning "movement."

My father could walk into a room and dominate any conversation whether it was with a Nobel laureate or a musician. He could turn a whiteboard into a mystical landscape. I could only imagine the brashness of his youthful career at the National Bureau of Standards (now called NIST). When he became too old to travel, he convinced my sister to scuba dive into an underwater volcano to measure its energetics. I sat in the dinghy counting the bubbles.

For relaxation, my father swam and played the mandolin. He wrote a paper with neurophysiologist Warren McCulloch on the concept of reverie — a state where the brain is "lost in thought." I think it was the

iii

many hours of swimming laps in a state of reverie where my father explored the cosmos — its components and its cycles — developing the ideas put forth here and in his hundreds of papers.

This book is a collection of his essays that lay out the foundations of homeokinetics. I have edited the essays for clarity. Whatever kind of scientist you are, this is the book to start with. The early chapters are an overview. Lessons 2-4 are a short remedial course in physics for the non-physicist reader. Applied scientists in fields such as biology, economics, anthropology, political science, physiology, and experimental psychology can learn the basic principles of physics there. Lessons 5-6 provide the basics of a homeokinetic approach to complex systems. These chapters are for everyone, but particularly for physicists. The appendix contains the brilliant paper Harry and my father wrote for *Science*.

Thea Iberall
Medfield, MA

CONTENTS

WHAT IS HOMEOKINETICS?

Homeokinetics is the study of complex systems—universes, galaxies, social systems, people, or even systems that seem as simple as gases. The approach models the entire universe as atomistic-like units bound in interactive ensembles that form systems, level by level in a nested hierarchy. Homeokinetics treats all complex systems on an equal footing, both animate and inanimate, providing them with a common viewpoint. The complexity in studying how they work is reduced by the emergence of common languages for all complex systems.

In order to use homeokinetics principles to study a particular complex system (e.g., a galaxy, a political system, etc), at least two scientists are needed: one who is versed in physics and irreversible thermodynamics; the other is trained in that specialty (what I call the 'flatland' science). As a physicist

1

working with flatland scientists, I realized that my colleagues need to have some understanding of physics principles. Therefore, I offer these lessons as a course of study with various general and specific applications.

THE BIRTH OF HOMEOKINETICS[1]

*"The department of history needs to concert with
the departments of biology, sociology and
psychology some common formula...and this
figure must be brought into accord with the
figures or formulas used by the department of
physics."*
- Henry Adams (1838-1918)
A Letter to American Teachers of History (1910)

---

[1]Revised and extracted from *Primer on Homeokinetics: A Physical
Foundation for Complex Systems*, Cri-de-Coeur Press, *Laguna Woods,
CA, 1998.* And from *A Course of Study on Homeokinetics: The
Physics of Complex Systems: Introduction, Bulletin 1, 1997*

Calls for a Common Science

Omitting earlier history, the 20th century provides perhaps four examples of manifestos calling for a common formula for science.

One is Henry Adams' letter calling for history teachers to work with physicists on the basis of a thermodynamics of historical processes. He argued that college history courses should include teaching of the second law of thermodynamics, which is the unstoppable tendency of energy to become less useful. Order becomes disorder, and he felt a theory of history should take this into account.

A second is a three-day symposium in 1939 called *Temperature, its Measurement and Control in Science and Industry*, sponsored by the American Institute of Physics. It had cooperation from the National Bureau of Standards (NBS), National Research Council, 12 engineering societies, and other agencies and companies. I started work at the NBS the year following this symposium and most of my technical mentors were contributors to that meeting. Its manifestos still ring in my memory banks.

The third overt manifesto is found in John Quincy Stewart's *The Development of Social Physics* (Stewart 1950). Stewart (1894-1972) was an American astrophysicist and engineer who pioneered work in social physics (or social mechanics as he later called it) which is the study of social phenomena from the perspective of physics.

A fourth is one by one of our mentors, Edward Uhler Condon (1902-1974), who dropped two issues of *Review of Modern Physics* onto my desk in 1952 and I was exposed to the world of biophysics. Biophysics, first termed in 1892, is an interdisciplinary science that uses methods from physics to study biological systems.

At NBS, I measured atmospheric and compressed gases, using kinetic theory to develop instrumentation covering the major variables of pressure, temperature, density, and flow, both steady state and dynamically changing. These variables often had to relate to atmospheric pressure—altitude up to perhaps 60 miles. The aircraft industry depended on these products. So did meteorologists for weather prediction and the military for high speed and altitude performance. These applied problems led to high speed so-called speed-of-sound rates of flow, to more than one phase flow (e.g., gases and liquids), two or more stream flow theory, metastability, solid state metals research both for steady state loads and dynamic (or changing) states. This irrevocably led to the problem of turbulence as distinguished from laminar flow. That also led to the full Navier-Stokes equation set, a nonlinear high ordered mathematical physical construct that still leaves much to be desired in solution.

From a homeokinetic perspective, these Navier-Stokes equations connect the lower level atomistic-like components with the upper level collective processes in the material-energetic substance.

In 1956, I was involved in the running of a famous boundary layer symposium in Freiburg sponsored by the International Union of Pure and Applied Physics (IUPAP). Such sponsorship lends considerable credence to the homeokinetics claim of a need for both 'pure' and engineering physics for complex problems. There, in Freiburg, the entire hydrodynamic clan including the first USSR contingent after Stalin's death, gathered to try to unravel some core of the Navier-Stokes problem after its first 100 years struggle.

Homeokinetics, not yet quite born, also had to struggle with the shadow of the safe human operation in space. Occupied during WW II with the problem of humans at high altitude and in space for the U.S. Navy and Air Force, by 1947 I suggested to the Navy that it was time to begin the development of spacesuits. At the *1998 Homeokinetics Conference* at the University of Connecticut, people from an array of scientific disciplines lent witness to the difficulty of that human-machine linkage problem.

It was in these more interdisciplinary explorations that our definition of complexity and its complexity measure began to emerge between 1955 and 1980. We were observing an area that physics has neglected, that of complex systems with their very long internal factory day delays. We were observing systems associated with nested hierarchy and with an extensive range of time scale processes. It was such connections, referred to as both up-down or in-out connections (as nested hierarchy) and side-side or flatland physics among atomistic-like components (as heterarchy[2]) that became the hallmark of homeokinetic problems. By 1975, we began to put a

---

[2]The word heterarchy was coined by Warren McCulloch (1898-1969) to describe the collective organization of the human brain (McCulloch 1945)

formal catch-phrase name on those complex problems. We associated them with *nature, life, humankind, mind*, and *society*.

Our Use of Engineering and Pure Physics

In introducing the propositional calculus in a basic book in metamathematics, Stephen Cole Kleene (1909-1994) defines mathematic or symbolic logic as logic treated by mathematical methods, noting that the book is also a study of logic used in mathematics. He immediately confronts the paradox: "...how can we treat logic mathematically (or in any systematic way) without using logic in the treatment?" He goes on to say that the solution of this paradox is simple. We put the logic we're studying into one compartment, and the logic we're using to study it in another. These "compartments," he informs us, are "languages." The language we use for study is the observer's or metalanguage. The language we study is the object language and the object logic. Thus, the metalanguage and its logic are capable of developing mathematical methods which can be used to study symbolic logic.

On another hand, Bertrand Russell (1872-1970) and Alfred North Whitehead (1861-1947) use the propositional calculus to derive the fundamental set properties of numbers and thereby serve up an introduction to mathematics. Russell always maintained that mathematics and logic are identical.

We operate from a related point of view. We do not intend to broker mathematics or logic. We are willing to accept what experts in those fields say their foundation or foundations are. But then we permit ourselves the required mathematical-logical mind

7

space to move somewhat off their bases to accommodate the laws and principles of physics.

The major method of exposition that we shall use is a combination of engineering physics and a more academic pure physics. We intend to show that we use and have to use both to produce a physical science for complexity. We strongly believe that explanations for complex systems lie in the many details that have to be assembled. On the pure side, our 'god' figures are, among others, Newton and Einstein. In engineering physics, we think of Theodore von Kármán (1881-1963), Ludwig Prandtl (1875-1953), Edgar Buckingham (1867-1940), and Charles Proteus Steinmetz (1865-1923).

References

Adams, Henry. *A Letter to American Teachers of History.* Washington, 1910. archive.org/details/ alettertoamerica00adamuoft

American Institute of Physics, *Temperature, its Measurement and Control in Science and Industry,* New York, Reinhold Publishing Corp., November 1939.

Stewart, John Q., The Development of Social Physics, *American Journal of Physics,* May 1950, Volume 18, Issue 5, pp. 239.

International Union of Pure and Applied Physics Symposium 1956, Freiberg.

LESSON 1
OVERVIEW OF HOMEOKINETICS

Physics is a science based on observation and experiment. From such data, it attempts to arrive at a set of principles adequate to recognize, describe, and relate all phenomena. Specifically, it attempts to deal with equilibria (with and without movement) and change in all material-energetic systems.

Complex Systems

A *system* (see definitions at end of this lesson) is a group of relatively common atomisms organized into a high-ordered atomism bounded from above and below in the space and time domain. Current comprehension identifies a nested – hierarchical – structure of a cosmos, nesting galaxies involving a *richness of intragalactic structures.* Continuing below, one finds molecules, atoms, nuclei, and fundamental particles, and an end in a rich complex *vacuum* below.

It has long been surmised that such nesting can be identified as an alternation of systems and their lower level—a level consisting of components that are more atomistic-like. Thus, associations of *atomisms* and *collectives* is an apt description. An earlier age was able to identify a concept of turtles all the way down, or sphere within sphere in a geometry of nested forms.

Normal physics deals with processes at single levels—cosmological physics, stellar physics, and the like—and also with the relation between systems and their lower levels, but only when the lower level atomisms are simple enough.

At some levels, systems are found involving very extended time scales among their atomistic processes. It is such levels that we consider to be *complex* in nature. They have extensive field memory functions; they use *languages*; they appear to direct their activities almost with purpose. We do not accept any mystification of their internal actions. We prefer to consider their interiors to be complex factories, and to involve complex *factory day processes*.

As a catch phrase, we refer to these complex systems as nature, life, humankind, mind, and society. Thus, they fall under biophysics, geophysics, social physics, ecological physics, evolutionary physics, and the like. In common with their simpler counterparts, complex systems:

- exhibit rest phases, smooth or creeping flows, turbulence, and chaotic phases.
- alternate in storminess and placidity, and in their intermittence and changeability.

It is the hierarchical character of such systems, with both side-side and in-out component processes, that interest us.

Homeokinetics is the study of complex systems, systems such as universes, galaxies, social systems, or various planetary subsystems. The entire universe thus consists of atomistic-like units—*atomisms*—bound in interactive ensembles to form systems, level by level in a nested hierarchy of systems.

The Story of the Collective

A person is a system, bounded in time and space from above and below. Skin is the border, separating the inside from the outside. The person's life is bounded in time from birth to death. When the person gets into a car, the person and the car become another system. The car joins other cars and forms another system called traffic. The flow of cars in a traffic system is much like the flowing of blood cells through our veins. Cars lose their autonomy in traffic and become part of a greater whole, just as blood cells do in our blood.

Within the system, atomisms as actors are moving. Whatever the level, whether the actors are people, cars, cells, or planets, they move. Early beliefs held that the movement of the actors was generated by a 'spirit', or 'anima'. This ancient idea of activation of things "out there" was by a spirit or spirits which thereby induced motion. Later, Aristotle introduced the notion of force as an agent of change, for example, in motion. From there, classical mechanics emerged with Newton's laws of motion.

The creation of the action by the actor is done by the internal *forces* acting on or within the actor.

There are ultimately very few forces or agents causing this. In fact, there are only four known forces:

- gravitational,
- electrical,
- strong nuclear, and
- weak nuclear forces.

People walk due to small electrical signals from the brain telling their leg muscles to contract. This throws them off balance and gravity takes over pulling them forward. An automobile has an internal combustion engine, which is driven by an electric spark that creates an explosion in the cylinder. The resulting movement of the piston in the cylinder is translated into rotary movement of the wheels, driving the car forward. Inside the human body, heart muscles contract as a result of an electrical signal from the autonomic nervous system. Movement of blood is created by the pumping action of the heart.

When the actors move, they interact with other actors. Examples include actors performing on a stage, people conversing in a car, blood cells coursing through veins, planets orbiting around a sun. In all these, interactions between actors occur. Two people see each other in a bar, walk over, talk, and then perhaps dance together. Two cars avoid a collision by veering away from each other. Two blood cells bump into each other as they travel through a small capillary. The actors are engaging in a game. This game, within any system, may be called 'Banging into Each Other by Pairs.' The agents (forces) guarantee that the actors will bang into each other. A few major things are conserved during this game:

- the sum of the paired mass (or matter) is conserved,
- the sum of energy is conserved,

- the sum of momentum (or movement) is conserved,
- and the sum of the electric charge is conserved.

For example, flip a coin. You and the coin exchange. The coin goes upward due to the momentum imparted to the coin by your thumb. Gravity pulls the coin back down in an exchange with the Earth. When a ball is thrown against a wall, momentum drives it towards the wall, which imparts motion to it in the opposite direction. Neither momentum nor matter is lost.

To describe the behavior of a system, then, one looks at how the flow of matter, energy, momentum, and electric charge spread out in this game that the actors within the system are playing. The purpose of the action is to tell the story of the collective. For a group of molecules in a balloon, the story of the collective may be to 'form a gas.' As a result of playing the game by the sharing of motion through their conservations, they all achieve the same temperature — or essentially the same energy. Now, if you want to face them, you will have to face them as a collective. You are no longer dealing with single atomisms.

How can one know that? Open a hole on that balloon and it will deflate. That simple interactive motion creates the collective's characteristics.

At a collective level, the story of the collective force is the social pressure. One can tell a human army, a gang, or a group to 'go kill' or 'go build a nation' and the bunch will walk out together and act no longer as individuals, but as a collective.

13

A Homeokinetic Vocabulary

We continue the lesson by expanding on the meanings of the vocabulary we've been introducing.

System A group of relatively common atomisms organized into a high-ordered atomism bounded from above and below in the space and time domain.

Atomism The word is used to denote both the doctrine and the object, like the usage of the word organism. An atomism denotes an atomic-like entity. It is a limited object of any size which is largely repeated in structure and character. It can withstand forces of interaction, such as collisions or other stresses, up to some level without breaking or cracking or otherwise permanently deforming. Yet it can bind with some of its counterparts or comparable units. It can possess and share mass, energy, momentum, or electric charge.

A very important part of its specification is that, like other so-called Brownian particles, it can share its energy and actions with other smaller atomisms underlying it. This nested character was developed first observationally by the botanist Robert Brown (1773-1858) in 1827 and then provided a theoretical account by Albert Einstein (1879-1955) in 1905. It has inspired us to the generality of how and why complexity of movement and change can be maintained at and among systems at all levels. Reproduced in the appendix of this book, our paper Soodak and Iberall (1978) offers a series of fundamental propositions about complex atomistic systems. Iberall and Soodak (1978) provides mathematical details for the propositions.

Collective In physical systems, pairs of atomistic particles can involve forces between them. In a group of such particles, the paired forces drive the system of particles to a collective motion. It is part of the character of physics to be able to identify such collective motions, such as the motion of a star, galaxy, rock, or stream of water. More generally, in complex systems, we are concerned with their collective stream of action.

Complex Complexity has many meanings. We elect to assign the notion of complexity in a physical system to processes of exchange among the atomisms of the collective which are much more extensive in time than their atomistic collisions. We imply nothing mysterious about the process except that the interior of those atomisms are each complex factory systems.

Factory Day Process What marks a factory is a large number of machines and engines performing a great number of processes spread out spatially at many operating stations, and temporally linked in a large up-down hierarchy of processes. Raw materials have to be brought in, stored, operated upon. Subparts have to be produced. Sales, accounting, and production processes have to take place as products are made and shipped. The processes are spread over an extensive physical domain and they are hierarchically linked and connected to satisfy scheduling and flows at a great number of time scales.

In our physical construct for complex systems, our complex atomisms are always such factories. Since another characteristic of a factory is that it has a total—often called bottom line—performance which tends to define the operational time scale, we have referred to that as the characteristic factory day. For many human-made systems, such a factory day is the Earth year. But for complex atomisms in nature, it can be anything from very small fractions of a second to the life-time scale of the universe.

Force In modern times, the notion of force 'caused' by direct action, or action at a distance, was introduced by Sir Isaac Newton (1642-1727). This made understanding the nature of forces hard. Where do forces reside? Is the force a property of the actors? When two actors are about to collide, a force builds up between them (e.g., gravity between the Earth and moon). As they approach collision, that imminent process potentially involves some sort of virtual exchange with the vacuum. It is theorized that during the collision and its approach, there is a virtual material-energetic force carrier emergent from the vacuum. These have been identified for the force between electric charges (the virtual photon), gravity (the graviton), and weak nuclear forces (the w and z bosons), and strong nuclear forces (gluons). Still missing is a demonstration of the graviton.

Richness of intragalactic structures The structures that astronomers and astrophysicists have identified are gas and dust clouds, stars, planetary systems, planets, planetismals, and comets. Planets nest many subsystems such as local gas, liquid and solid systems, including a rich geophysics and chemistry, as well as a rich biophysics and chemistry, supporting life, its command-control and social systems and processes.

Language If one understands the extensive space and time processing in complex factories, and the requisite and extensive field memory function to achieve all those processes, then language becomes a catalytic process that evokes action or potential images of action. What a catalyst will do is speed or slow down a 'chemical' reaction. That is what our language usages do in living systems at various levels. We speak to our organs, our cells, and to each other, and that controls the flow of our collective actions both in space and in time.

Field Memory Function A complex field factory system, involving extensive forces operating at a great number of scales, has to be endowed with a memory. The question, without invoking human animation, is what serves as memory? The answer is that factory processes themselves — derived from the forces — map out such memory functions. This is just as true in any human-made system as in any natural-made system. The possibility of factors existing in human society or in nature involving an extended factory day process implies that there will be a great number of memory functions, spread out in space and time. For example, John Von Neumann (1903-1957) used a circulating flow system for a short term memory in computers, and he used storage in magnetic domains for long term storage. In the body, we store more commonly as short-lived and long-lived molecules. Systems can use any material or energetics at hand for such memory functions.

Vacuum The quantum vacuum is not the completely empty space visualized in the 19th century. In quantum theory, the quantum state of lowest energy of any system — even that of a simple mechanical oscillator — is generally not one of zero energy. The vacuum is thus a quantum state in which the total energy of all fundamental fields of nature is a local minimum, smaller than the energy of all slightly different states. It thus contains all fundamental fields — those of the fundamental particles (e.g., quarks and leptons) and those of the field quanta — through which the particles interact with each other by strong, electromagnetic, weak, and gravity force.

It is conceivable that other local minimum states much different from our current vacuum can exist or did exist in some past stage of our expanding universe. In fact, a transition from a possibly initial vacuum state to the current one shortly after the initiation of the big bang is the basis of the inflationary model of the universe — the model that goes a long way toward explaining why our patch of the universe, out to the relativistic horizon, is very homogeneous and isotropic on the large scale.

Summary

A complex system is one where there is a tremendous amount of internal exchange by the actors. The physics of complex systems is played out on the basis of trying to understand what these complex internal agents are doing.

Ordinary physics is a flatland physics—by that, we mean a physics at some particular level. For example, nuclear physics deals with the constituents and interactions of atomic nuclei. Atomic physics studies atoms. Biophysics studies biological systems; social physics studies social phenomena; stellar physics studies the stars. Atoms are not stars—they are at different levels.

Homeokinetic physics combines flatland physics with the study of the up-down processes that binds the levels. Tools, such as mechanics, quantum field theory, and the laws of thermodynamics, provide key relationships for the binding of the levels, how they connect, and how the energy flows up and down. And whether the atomisms are atoms, molecules, cells, people, stars, galaxies, or universes, the same tools can be used to understand them. Homeokinetics treats all complex systems on an equal footing, animate and inanimate, providing them with a common viewpoint. The complexity in studying how they work is reduced by the emergence of common languages in all complex systems.

References

Iberall, Arthur and Harry Soodak. Physical Basis for Complex Systems—Some Propositions Relating levels of Organization. *Collective Phenomena* 3 (1978), pp. 9-24.

Soodak, Harry and Arthur Iberall. Homeokinetics: A Physical Science for Complex Systems, *Science*, 18 August, 1978, Vol. 201, No. 4356, pp. 579-582. (see Appendix).

LESSON 2
ONE SCIENCE — PHYSICS[3]

"How can I or anyone else claim that there is a set of principles, so embracing, that it can apply to all systems, simple and complex, living and nonliving, small and large? That arises because there is one science that is first among all the others. That science is physics — the laws of motion and change in all systems."

Aristotle (384-322 BC)

So said the Greek philosopher-scientist Aristotle 2300 years ago. We physicists believe that the reality of that promise has been amply realized by the further contributions made by Sir Isaac Newton, James Clerk Maxwell (1831-1879), and Albert Einstein. As mentioned, physics has been used to study stars, atoms, atomic nuclei, and biological systems. But can

[3]Revised from *One Science – Physics, CP2: Commentaries – Physical and Philosophic Vol. 1. No. 1 Society 1.1, 1990*

the principles be so embracing as to apply to all systems, even perhaps something called social physics? And is it possible to do it in such simple terms that its applicability and rightness will become adequately apparent? What would a social physics look like?

Merriam-Webster defines society as "an enduring and cooperating social group whose members have developed organized patterns of relationships through interaction with one another." Predicting people's behavior isn't as easy as predicting the behavior of a motor, say, or a radio. These mechanical devices were designed for a specific reason and come with user manuals. People don't. They interact, they have emotions and needs. And yet, in this monograph, you will begin to see how the principles of physics can be applied to any complex system, even one, for example, as complex as a society.

Forces as Agents of Change

Physics states that forces are agents of change, and change causes movement. Atoms, particles of dust, ping-pong balls, living cells, people, even stars — are all engaged in motion. When they move freely, we can imagine that there are no forces acting on them (for the moment, we will ignore gravitational and electrical forces). At some point in time, one of these items will collide with another. A force will arise — a mutual mechanical force of collision. Such a force causes a change in motion. They each redirect their movement and continue again until they collide once more in new pairs.

Let us now examine what happens during the

time of collision. There are three equivalent views of such an effector of change.

1. In the most direct view, the action of a force is to change the motion; that is, to make the item accelerate. You push on a thing, it jerks forward by a change in motion.

2. In the second view, the effect of a force acting for a time is to change the motion more directly. Multiplying the amount (or measure) of that force by the measure of the time it acts is known as the *impulse*. The impulse changes the item's momentum. **Momentum** describes how fast the item is moving (as opposed to acceleration, which is how fast the velocity changes). Momentum is the velocity of movement multiplied by the *mass* of the item (mass is how much matter it contains).

Humans engage in this process all the time. If you swing a baseball bat or a golf club at a ball, the impulse changes the momentum of the struck object. Remember, the impulse is the collisional force multiplied by the time that force acted. If the object is massive like a big chair or big ball, the change in velocity is of lesser magnitude for the same impulse. You can try it yourself. Slap a ball against a wall and see how the impulse of your slap starts the ball moving. See then how the impulse from the wall changes the momentum of the ball as it bounces back from the wall.

Impulse = force x time
Momentum = mass x velocity

3. In a third view, the effect of a force acting through a distance is to change the *energy of motion* of the item on which the force acted. For example, pushing or pulling a box on the ground for some distance changes the box's energy. Multiplying the measure of the force and the distance through which the force acted is known as the *work* done on the item. The energy of motion is measured by the product of half the mass of the item multiplied by the velocity repeated twice.

> Work = force x distance
>
> Energy = ½ mass x velocity²

To summarize, physics is concerned with forces acting in space and time on masses of matter. That is from where the changes in motion arise. Now, we continue on to discuss the subsequent motion caused by the collision.

Conservations of Motion

The forces of collision come in pairs (one hits the other and the other hits the one), and as a result, the forces are equal and opposite. This is Newton's third law of motion. And since the forces are equal and opposite, their effect on the pair of colliding particles is nil, or zero. Therefore, the paired aspects of their motion have not changed. Since each of the force collisions that occurred involved a distance of collision (the work done by the collision) and a time of collision (the impulse of the collision), we can state that:

- the pair of particles did not accelerate;
- the momentum of the pair of particles did not change; and
- the energy of the pair of particles did not change.

Also, there was no reason for the mass of the pair of particles to change. Thus, even though the independent motions of each of the particles in the pair did change, the composite measures of the pair did not.

From this analysis, we infer that there were three fundamental properties of the pair that did not change. Those properties are known as the *fundamental conservations of the motion of collision*. The three measures that were conserved are:

- the measures of their matter (before, during, and after the collision),
- the measures of their momentum, and
- the measures of their energy of motion.

As a result of the fact that three such conservations exist, we can determine the motion of the colliding pair of particles due to collisions pair by pair. Watch any ball player, yourself or perhaps your skilled children, or any golfer, or any pool player. They are computing these properties of collisions each time they exert a colliding force on some object. While the mathematical expression of collisional forces and conservations is perhaps frightening, it doesn't take mathematics for a three year old to begin to demonstrate objective skills of performance in accordance with these principles. Nor does it in non-humans, for example, in a bat echolocating, a hawk swooping on its prey, or a monkey jumping from tree to tree.

Why does all this matter? Let us think for a minute how we can use these principles in studying various systems. In a gas, we use it to describe one collision between two atoms or molecules; of course, there are billions of billions of billions of such particles. In a galaxy, we would use it to study the billions of billions of stars interacting. In a living organism, we would use it to study billions of cells interacting. In these examples, there is more going on than just the effect of one pair of colliding particles. But here again, the principles of physics come to the rescue and tell us how to describe the multiplicity of all the pairs of interaction.

Atomisms

In the most general sense, that multiplicity of all the pairs of interaction is known as the connection between the micro and the macro — the little and the big, the local and global. For the micro game, we refer to the play as the resulting *kinetic or dynamic interaction* among atomisms. *Atomisms* are the generalized description of atomic-like or atomistic "things": the things that banged into each other in interaction without necessarily getting destroyed.

The atomic doctrine was first developed by the classical Greeks who sought out the primitive particles or material substances that might arise with indefinite division of material objects. They could not fully decide how many such particles there were nor what those particles were. We know now that such atomistic particles come in nested levels, making up a complex hierarchy of such units. For example, we have a cosmos which comprises perhaps one or more universes. Within any such universe, there are galaxies. These galaxies comprise large collections of interacting stars and cold matter. In and among that matter, there are a variety of other intragalactic matter systems — planets, planetismals, clouds, and chemical systems such as geochemical and biochemical systems. Within these, there are atoms, ions, and molecules.

The smallest level we know at the moment are the leptons and quarks, all in a so-called vacuum. According to our current demonstrations and understanding, the result of interactions among leptons and quarks is to produce the same or other leptons and quarks from the vacuum. At present, we can't find anything or things below them.

At each level are the units — a cosmos, a universe, a galaxy, a planet, a human, an atom, a lepton. These are the atomisms of the nested level. At the level most interesting for us in this study at the moment, we wish to concentrate on the biochemical systems which include us and our societies.

Note that the macro-micro game among the atomisms and their organized field of play is much more extensive than any simple game that people play. Consider a game of baseball. We may consider one interaction to be a batter facing an opposing team of 9 players. In 9 inning turns, three players from each of the two sides up at bat have to be put out in turn, starting from play initiated by a pitcher who is manipulating the throw of a ball by the laws of physics. Thus a game, minimally, involves 54 playing interactions, in which every batter is put out in turn.

But that is not the total play. Since the batters may score base hits rather than be put out, many more than 54 turns at bat are taken. It is more like 100-200 turns at bat that are taken. One hundred years have not exhausted the amount of drama this game can create. Yet that game is extraordinarily simpler than any natural atomistic system of field play. Nevertheless, physics can collapse the play of one of these mammoth field games to a relatively small measure.

Flow fields

Imagine watching water flowing past a ship's propeller. You are looking at what is called in physics a *flow field* – the result of the pair-by-pair motional interactions of water molecules. You can see flow fields being produced by mechanical fans, water pumps, and hair dryers. Also, by turbine-driven aircraft, reaction spacecraft, rotationally-driven galaxies, nuclear reaction-driven stars. You see it in the flow in a river, the tides in the ocean. In more general terms, a flow field is a *field phenomenon* – which is the organized play of a large ensemble of players interacting through an extended space-time field of motional action among them. A flow field is likely the most common of all physical field phenomena. So how does one describe its general phenomena of motion?

Quantifying Motion

In order to understand the more general motion of the entire field of players, we'll start by introducing an intermediate description of the local ensemble. Let us imagine a local space-time box in which a considerable number of interacting plays are taking place. Look at it as a small local ballfield or a portion of a street where a ballgame is going on. Namely, there are a considerable number of players in the spatial box which only occupies a small amount of space, and we are going to observe the motion in that fixed box over a considerable length of time. In addition, we are only going to examine the motion at certain intervals of time (e.g., every other inning, etc.).

What we get out of those discrete, intermittent observations are local averages, the statistics that everyone who lives in that neighborhood knows. For example, every time we blink — making one of our intermittent observations — we can count how many particles are in the box. Or, as an equivalent measure, we can count how much matter (mass) these particles have contributed to the content of the box. Those counts give us one local measure — the local density.

Note that we will either have the number density or the mass density. Suppose you imagined the box to be one cubic inch in volume (1 inch by 1 inch by 1 inch), and you counted 10 particles in the box, or 10 grams in the box (the mass of a U.S. nickel is about 5 grams). Then we could say that the number density is 10 particles per cubic inch; or the matter density is 10 grams per cubic inch. If we kept counting the contents of the box at different observation times, each time perhaps finding a different number — say 10, 13, 11,

15, 13, 11, 13, 10 — we could count up the total 96 and divide that by the number of observations 8, and get an average, 12. This is a statistic. We would then say that the average density (number or mass) is 12 per cubic inch.

In the same way, we could get the average for the amount of momentum that is to be found in this local box. We get that average by adding up how much momentum each particle carries when we look at it. Then, similarly, we could find the average energy of motion in the box.

Conservations for Ensemble

We saw earlier that three measures — mass, momentum, and energy — are conserved in pair by pair collisions. What about when we are observing local averages for a local ensemble of collisions? After all, we are no longer looking at just two particles. We have to extend our view to include the conservations across the group. Our local intermediate level of measures represents the local group conservations that are being carried on in the field of particles. In terms of physics, we can name these intermediate local measures:

1. *Density.* Corresponding to the conservation of number of particles or mass of particles, we have the local measure of density.
2. *Pressure.* Corresponding to the conservation of momentum, we have the pressure. Pressure represents how much momentum per unit wall surface per unit of time that the particles in any

extended region will deliver through any imagined wall space.

3. *Motional energy.* Corresponding to the conservation of motional energy of a pair of particles, we have the motional energy of the local group. Since it measures the energy associated with the specific volume, it is called the *specific energy.*

For pressure, think of it as the atomistic "balls" being engaged in a handball game against some imagined wall. Cap off the flow through a hose or through a hole in a pressurized container or balloon, and you can feel the pressure mount. It is the force per unit area of the hole that you had to exert to barely seal the hole off.

As for local energy, there is again an easy physical way to see it. Put your finger into that field of atomisms, and feel its *temperature* with your finger. That is a measure of the energy that the atomistic things carry. Of course, if we want the true measure of the specific energy, then the temperature is not enough. The specific energy is contained in the measure of the motional energy every which way that the atomistic thing can move. Temperature is a common equal measure of that motional energy in any one way of moving—what we call one *degree of easy freedom* to move. But we need to know how many degrees of easy freedom there are to move.

There are always at least three ways for a free body to move—forward-back, side-side, up-down. Any particle, however tiny, if free, can move in those directions. But a fair-sized ball can also spin in three ways, which adds three more ways to move. If an item has internal parts, there are also ways of shaking or vibrating or rotating or associating those parts.

The upshot of all these ways to move is that specific energy can range from 3 to 12 times the measure of energy of motion beyond what temperature by itself might permit if there were only one degree of motional freedom. For example, see how fast a thermometer (which is a known system that can be taken as a reference) moves toward the last few degrees of the current temperature. The measure we are going after is the so called *heat capacity*. This is a measure of how much energy you have to put in to something in order to raise its temperature, say, 1° C. That measure tells you how many degrees of freedom the energy could have. This is from 3 to 12 degrees of freedom.

In summary, we see that the atomistic group conservations, for a given ensemble of atomisms, can be represented by three local measures: density, pressure, and temperature.

Equation of State for Ensemble

These three local group averages for the three micro conservations are related in an invariant way. That relation is known as the *equation of state of the group or ensemble*. Let us think back to the little box in which we made the observations to determine the local averages. Think of many of these boxes. In every one of those freely connected and equally accessible boxes, the same equation of state exists. It no longer relates to only one box, but to all such boxes. There are many ball games going on throughout the whole field region. However, the individual group measures may vary from place and time to place and time. We will come back to this concept.

Why are these local conservation measures connected by an equation of state? It's because each time a new particle enters a box, it carries its number (or mass) count, its momentum count, and its energy count into the box. As long as these are the only conservational measures, then these three new fluctuations are connected just in the same way as the ones in the box already.

Now let us extend this analysis to larger items, such as baseball players. Suppose there are lots of baseball games going on. Each game is occurring in its box — the Yankees in Yankee Stadium, the Red Sox in Fenway Park, etc. All these games — as well as the teams, players, rules, and managers — are connected together into a league, and all the elements of play are, loosely speaking, comparably competent to continue playing. We don't want to know how to win one of the ball games, but instead, how to manage it with enough competence to stay in the play. We all know that there is no manager who can win all the time. You don't win them all, or get a hit every time at bat, or even put out a batter at every turn. Professional baseball has many statistics, many of which are recited repeatedly by people, particularly boys and their older counterparts, from perhaps eight years of age on up. They know how many hits a player can average and how many games a pitcher has won. Fans are always second guessing the manager. What can physics tell us that these avid observers do not know?

Ballplayers are not just any human beings; they are drawn from a special pool of people who can learn and acquire a particular set of skills. They also apply the laws of physics to produce different statistical results, something a manager is acutely aware of. For example, with ballplayers, you need to select them and use them so that they average nearly one hit per five times at bat with perhaps one third of them capable of producing one hit per three times at bat. You have to have a pool of pitchers who can pitch enough strikeouts and not give up too many hits, and you have to have fielders who don't make playing errors with more than a certain frequency of play.

These are mechanical tasks performable in rather narrow limits by only certain people. But they're also thermodynamic field tasks or processes: the ballplayer is converting mechanical energy from one level of the atomism to another, for example, transforming Wheaties to base hits and put outs, or transforming ball play to earned money, or ball play to a variety of internal emotions such as elation, satisfaction, and anxiety. All these processes are involved in managing a ball team.

And ultimately, whether we are looking at ball players or molecules in a gas or liquid, the players at any level in the atomistic hierarchy are engaged in a statistical mechanics-thermodynamics game with the same physics specialized for each of their games.

Constraints on Local Averages

We've examined the local connected averages in a simple flow field — density, pressure, and temperature or specific energy. When do we pay attention to temperature and when to specific energy? If we have selected our molecular player, say water molecules rather than oxygen or hydrogen molecules, temperature would be our third local measure. If we mix up the molecular players, then we have to take into account the specific molecular properties of their specific heat. This would be equivalent to the problem of managing a mixed group of players—say baseball, golf, and tennis players. Their actions work differently and have different worth.

An interesting point to note is that these local averages are connected. This means that if you elect two of them, the third one is prescribed. What does that mean?

Let's start with density. To do this, let's take a closed empty rigid container with some particular volume, say one liter. Now put a small amount of water in that container without any air. This is not as easy as it sounds. The easiest way to achieve this state without laboratory equipment is as follows: Start with a bottle which, of course, will have air in it, and put some water in the bottle. Begin to heat the bottle until the water boils out (you can use a double boiler to do this). If you put a flap on top of the bottle, perhaps hinging a cork as a cover, the water will boil out as steam with no air returning. When you have boiled all the water out until only steam remains, or boiled out some of the water until whatever amount of water you want to leave in the bottle, you can then seal it with a cork or stopper. Now let the water cool off, and you will have succeeded in the proposed task. Other ways might require a very good vacuum pump, a completely collapsible balloon later jammed into a box, a carefully constructed piston and cylinder, or heat and a system of valves. The amount of water (as liquid water or steam) that you put into or left in the container determines the density of water in that container. Namely, if you divide the measure of the mass of water in the container by the volume of the container, that measure gives you the average density of water in the container. That is how you managed to fix the density.

$$\text{Average density} = \text{mass/volume}$$

Next, let's fix the temperature. The easiest way would be to put the closed-off container into an oven or a refrigerator. Before doing this, put a thermometer into the appliance and adjust the temperature to the one you want the water to have. That fixes the temperature.

What about the pressure? You can determine what the pressure is in the container by measuring how much force is required to hold the lid sealed. However, you cannot fix the pressure in the container. It's fixed by the fact that:

(a) you filled the container with a specific number or mass of water molecules, the "things" you chose to manage, and

(b) you fixed the temperature

This fixes the pressure. That's the meaning of the equation of state for water.

Change the type of molecule and you would have

another equation of state for the other molecules (the change in the equation of state would depend on properties of the molecule).

Phases of Matter

Let's manage the contents of that bottle. For example, suppose we first made certain that the walls of the container were all held at the same temperature. How could we do that? By putting the container in a totally temperature-regulated bath — for example, a refrigerator or oven or a surround of gas or liquid (or even sand). After a certain amount of time, the internal temperature in the water will be the same as the wall's temperature. But now we find a surprise. At high temperature, we find that all the water is evaporated and the contents are only steam vapor. Also, we find that, as the temperature rises further, the pressure rises.

At sufficiently lowered temperature, we find a value at which steam starts to condense to droplets of water. The lower the temperature, the larger the pool of liquid droplets we find. Then — another surprise — we reach a temperature at which the droplets or pools of water freeze into a solid — water ice. There still is a "steam" vapor, but its vapor pressure has been diminishing all the way with temperature. (How do we know? Put in a surface much colder than the container temperature and you will see that "steam" or vapor condensing. You see such a process in the morning as the dew on the grass evaporates as soon as the surface warms up).

We can see that the equation of state for water or any other pure atomic or molecular substance can be rather complicated. Not only does the state of density, pressure, and temperature change, but also the phase of matter—gas, liquid, solid or combinations of these phases—can change with the state measures. We can manage to make pressure, temperature, and density do a versatile variety of things. Before refrigerators, for example, people used "ice boxes", where a piece of ice was put in a box, and even though the ice melted, it would keep the inside of the box cool, for example, near 32° F or 0° C. Another example: on a hot day, you can put on a wet shirt. As the water evaporates, it will cool you off.

To exemplify a little more versatility than we have so far shown for the equation of state, let us suppose that we raised the temperature of the water vapor to extremely high values. We would find that we could reach temperatures that would destroy the molecules. The high motional energy of the molecules banging into each other at high temperature would crack them apart, achieving a chemical reaction. The water molecules would change their chemical state and separate into oxygen and hydrogen. At another level, for example, eggs: you can burn the eggs you are frying. Or, we could add other ingredients to the water and cause it also to enter into other chemical reactions. So we see another aspect of an equation of state, the possibility for chemical changes in state. Chemistry, by definition, is the making, breaking and exchanging of bonds between atomistic components; this will remain true even when we deal with societies.

Creating Flow Fields

But let us now get to a more dynamic game, one worthy of being called fluid dynamics (a subdiscipline is hydrodynamics, from the Greek *hudro* meaning water). What we want to do is to take the changeable equation of state, changeable from time and place to time and place, and manage it to do things in time and place. Let us start simply. In the surface of a closed rigid container, prick a small hole. The rest of the container wall maintains its temperature and pressure. The pressure falls near the hole. What happens? There is a flow of momentum out of the hole. In time, the contents of the container loses its contained momentum; that is, its pressure falls. Its temperature doesn't have to fall. We could continue to keep the walls warm.

This simple example demonstrates that by changing the equation of state measures between different regions of a matter field, it is possible to create flow fields, for example, flows of density, flows of momentum, flows of energy.

Transport Measures

The descriptions of these flows are represented by equations of change. There are as many equations of change as there are conservations. In a simple flow field, we see:

- three local conservations (density, momentum, energy), and
- three equations of change, one globally (throughout the field) for each local pair by pair conservation. Namely, there is a flow of

mass or number, a flow of momentum, and a flow of energy.

The description of these processes is very complex, so we will just touch on them. Suffice it to say that depending on the atomistic material and its temperature or pressure range, there are *transport measures* that tell one something about the rules of flow. Transport measures are known as diffusivities. A *diffusion* is the process of spreading out or scattering:

- There is a measure for how fast one kind of atomism may move among other kinds. That is known as the **mass species diffusivity** (each type or species of atomism can have a different measure).

- There is a measure for how fast momentum will flow. That is known as the **momentum diffusivity**. The more common name is the *viscosity* of the fluid substance. Water, because of its great fluidity and low viscosity, relaxes quickly and diffuses its momentum slowly. Tar, because of its small fluidity and great viscosity, relaxes slowly and diffuses its momentum quickly.

- There is a measure for how fast energy will flow. That is known as the **energy diffusivity**. Its common name is the **thermal conductivity**. It tells you something about how fast you will say "ouch" when you touch a hot surface.

Examples of Managing Flow

Let us now illustrate how to manage these

processes independently. First, let us manage a flow itself, for example, the flow or diffusion of momentum.

Take a large container and pump it up with pressure. Suppose, first, that you keep the temperature of the container constant, or nearly constant. How? Leave it standing outside or put the container in a refrigerator or oven. Push a little amount of material into the container. For example, you can blow small amounts of air in, breath by breath. Or you can push a small amount of water in by using a pump or by pouring it in using the gravitational force. As you push the gas or liquid material in, you will begin to see the pressure rising. But think of using a very large container. It will take a long time to get the container or reservoir filled and the pressure high. But it will get there.

Now someplace in your reservoir, say near its bottom, make a hole, perhaps plug in a pipe and add a valve so that you have a hole that you can open and close. Here, then, you will see how the pressure in the reservoir creates a flow or diffusion of momentum from the hole, pipe, or valve. You are the manager of this system.

Is this real and practical? Of course. It is the way your city supplies water to every valve or faucet connected to its large reservoir. You don't win or lose in this game of managing such a flow supply, you just succeed in doing it.

Let's manage the flow another way, through temperature. This time fill up the reservoir, but don't pump up its pressure high. If, for example, you have water in the container, put the hole on top. Now heat the container so as to raise its wall temperature. Recall in the equation of state that with temperature rising, the pressure rises. After a while, the water is converted to steam and its pressure then creates a flow of momentum. That is, through manipulating the energy via temperature, we used the equation of state to transform that measure into pressure and then the pressure into a flow or diffusion of momentum.

Is this practical? Of course, it's the basis for the steam engine, also called the external combustion engine, because the driving heat came from outside and was applied to the container walls. Such a container is known as a "boiler." You likely have one in your house. It may be used in a combined fashion, partly used as a reservoir of pressure and partly as a reservoir for heat energy to give you hot water or steam flow.

This suggests a third way to create a flow or diffusion of momentum. This is by a process of *chemical conversion*.

This time, insert a mix of two substances, say liquid gasoline and air. With an igniting hot spot (high temperature) produced somewhere in the mix, these two different sorts of molecules may undergo a chemical process. In the case of a simple fuel and oxygen, the chemical process is one of breaking and exchanging fractions of each type of molecule. But that process gives off heat energy, and that heats up the old and new molecules. Then, as before, that raises the temperature of the materials. That raised temperature raises the pressure, because the density was fixed, and creates a flow.

Is this practical? Yes, it is what happens in each cylinder of an automobile engine many times per second. A small amount of fuel and air is pumped into the cylinder. It is sparked electrically to start a combustion. The fuel and air "explode," producing high temperature and pressure. That pushes the little cylinder container into a larger volume configuration via a piston-like motion. That spins the crankshaft and wheels. After each such explosion, the flow products are exhausted out the tail pipe. This device is called an internal, rather than an external, combustion engine, because the management took place among the players. (A diesel engine doesn't use a heating spark to ignite the fuel. It just compresses the mixture enough which then explodes chemically).

Here is another way to create a flow of momentum. We place a series of blades mounted on a shaft, at an angle to the shaft. Now, if we turn the shaft (a mechanical motion), those blades will "grab" the air and force it into motion. This occurs because of a *flow boundary condition*. If we move a sheet of atoms or molecules past other sheets, the one sheet will drag the other sheet. This is due to a dynamic transport property of matter, in this case the momentum diffusivity or viscosity. To make this work fairly well, the sheet of molecules used for the drive was the surface of a solid, so that they remained united and stuck together. The molecules of the fluid that we dragged the solid sheet past could not oppose that motion too strenuously, so they had to move. That created a flow or diffusion of momentum.

Is that practical? Of course, those blades may be a propeller or turbine in an airplane or a ship and they create the flow stream that makes the craft move. Here the momentum transfer was rather direct. When an entire ensemble of players are forced into motion directly, shepherded, that is known as *convection* rather than diffusion.

Let's look at a final example that appears to be made more indirect, and therefore, is a little more subtle.

Let's take two containers. Let's join them on a common smooth face, say by abutting them together. We will fill each container with a different molecular substance, say one oxygen and the other nitrogen, or one water and the other oil. We'll arrange to have the same pressure in both containers, as weak or strong as you want. To do this, we could open holes in both containers, suspend a weighted and tapered piston in each hole, and keep filling both containers till the same weight in each piston "floats." You see this example in a pressure cooker. The weight of the float, for a given area of vent hole, determines the "pressure" of which the float rises and vents material. We will also arrange the same temperature bath on both sides.

Now open a hole or a pipe between the two containers. With the same pressure and temperature on both sides, you might think that nothing will change. But it will. Substance 1 will diffuse into substance 2, and vice versa. Because of the difference of materials, there will be matter or mass diffusion, which thus creates a momentum diffusion of each substance separately.

Is this real? Certainly. Every time you put milk or cream or sugar in your coffee, you see the process taking place without stirring. How do you think the water that rains on Earth gets back into the atmosphere? Largely by that evaporative, diffusion, process.

Summary

In summary, we have set forth basic principles of physics that we believe can apply, as Aristotle said, "to all systems, simple and complex, living and nonliving, small and large." An equation of state captures the relation among atomistic conservations. There are equations of change which you can manipulate from "outside" (at the walls) or "inside" (as a player) to manage and influence the play in space or time throughout the field. You can transform any one of the conservations, stationary (static) or changing (dynamic), into any of the other conservations, in a different static or dynamic form. This is flow or field physics, and it provides us with a set of starting tools to manage a complex system, even one such as a society, an enduring and cooperating social group.

LESSON 3
THERMODYNAMICS[4]

Introduction

Sir Isaac Newton spoke of forces as the "active agents of nature." He said that, in a forceless universe, nothing would really be happening, even though there might be a vast number of particles all moving along their straight inertial paths at constant speed. Collisions could not occur because force is required to change either the speed or direction of a particle motion. Indeed, it is the action of forces of attraction that lead to the formation of objects (e.g., galaxies, stars, humans, atoms, nuclei). It is the action of forces of repulsion that almost always balances with forces of attraction in order to prevent matter from coming together and 'densifying' without limit. It is the action of forces that pump our blood, move

---

[4]Revised from *Thermodynamics, CP2: Commentaries – Physical and Philosophic Vol. 1. No. 1 Society 1.1, 1990*

our muscles, and send our nerve signals.

It's a very large leap from the action of two atoms attracting each other to form a molecule or that of two colliding atoms or molecules rebounding from each other, to the actions of individual humans and their interactions in small and large social groupings. The leap must be made in stages. At this point, suffice it to say that it's the action of biological and social 'forces' that move people to act, behave, vote, and feel the way they do.

While not as obvious to the non-physicist, it is already a large leap from the interaction between two atoms or simple molecules to the behavior of a macroscopically large number of interacting atoms or molecules as in a gas. In this essay, we describe:

a. the basic *physics of interaction* between two simple 'particles',
b. the strategy of describing the *macroscopic properties* of a large number of such particles, and
c. the *relation* between the macroscopic description and the microscopic physics of particle-particle interaction.

Thermodynamics (from the Greek *therme*, meaning "heat" and *dynamis*, meaning "power") is the study of processes that involve changes in temperature, transformation of energy, the relationship between heat and work. It studies heat energy and its relation to macroscopic variables such as temperature, pressure, and volume. Thermodynamics is the macrophysics within and between organized levels. It will be our tool for studying societies and other complex systems.

Physics of Interaction — the Micro Level

Imagine a large number of simple particles, atoms, or molecules moving around in some space. To consider the simplest case, we assume that the forces of attraction between these particles are negligible. If we then follow the motion of any individual particle, we will see it undergoing a zigzag motion consisting of straight flights separated by rapid changes of direction. Each straight flight is the 'free flight' motion that takes place when no force is acting on the particle. By *Newton's first law of motion*, this takes place at constant *velocity*. The rapid changes of direction and of speed occur when the particle collides with another particle. The repulsive force between the colliding particles changes the speeds and directions of both particles. Think of billiard ball collisions as a well-known macroscopic example.

> Force = mass x acceleration
> Momentum = mass x velocity
> Impulse = force x time
> Kinetic energy = ½ mass x velocity²

According to *Newton's second law of motion*, a force on a particle causes its velocity to change at a rate given by the strength of the force divided by the mass of the particle. This rate is called the *acceleration*. The change in the velocity takes place in the direction of the force. A consequence of this law is the following: If we define the *momentum* of a particle as the product of its velocity and its mass, then the action of a force acting for a time is to change the momentum of the particle by an amount given by the product of the force and the time. This product is called the *impulse*.

But, according to **Newton's third law of motion**, forces between particles are always mutual and equal in strength and opposite in direction. It follows that two colliding particles repel each other with forces of equal strength and in opposite directions, and therefore change each other's momentum by equal amounts in opposite directions. Since momentum is a directional quantity (a so-called vector quantity), the sum of the momenta of the particles is the same after the collision as before. Total momentum is said to be *'conserved'*.

The total energy is also conserved. That is, the sum of the energies of the particles is the same after the collision as before. The energy of a stationary particle is called its *internal energy* — this is the energy of any and all actions taking place inside the 'particle'. The energy of its motion through space is called its **kinetic energy**, and it is equal to one half its mass times the square of its velocity. The energy of a moving particle is the sum of its internal energy and kinetic energy. The amount of energy transferred from one of the colliding particles to the other is given by the product of the force times the distance over which the force acts. If the collision is not intense enough to cause changes inside the particles, their internal energies are not altered, and then the sum of the kinetic energies of the particles is the same after the collision as before.

If we also assume that collisions are not intense

enough to destroy the particles (by breaking them into parts, for example), then the number of particles is always a conserved quantity. Collisions are then characterized by:

- conservation of matter content — particle number or total mass
- conservation of momentum, and
- conservation of energy.

If there are different types of particles (as in air), we give the number of each type in, say, a cubic inch of space. Alternatively, we can give the total mass of each type in a cubic inch. Either of these equivalent descriptions may be termed the *matter content*.

The Macro Level vs the Micro Level

Let us now leap from the micro to the macro — from the physics of the micro level as a succession of particle free flights and collisions, to the macro level description of a gas consisting of a great many interacting particles.

We point out that in one cubic inch of normal air there are about four hundred billion billion (4×10^{20}) molecules undergoing stereotypic actions — free flights of length on the order of a hundred thousandth (10^{-5}) of an inch at speeds on the order of ten thousand (10^4) inches per second (about 700 miles per hour). The duration of each free flight is then about a billionth of a second (or one nanosecond or 10^{-9}). Each molecule makes about a billion collisions each second. In a gas, the collision duration is a small fraction of the free flight time.

However, to quote Shakespeare, it is 'much ado about nothing.' Because, in spite of all the activity taking place in each small time interval in the cubic inch — all the collisions, all the changes in velocity of the individual particles, and all the changes in their energies — the values of the conserved quantities are unaffected by the interactions occurring inside the cubic inch. The content of the matter is unchanged, the total momentum is unchanged, the total energy is unchanged. What happens is that the total momentum is distributed by the collisions among all the particles in the cubic inch in some characteristic manner. Similarly, the total energy is distributed among the kinetic energies of all the particles, and among the internal energies that are excited in collisions.

It should be noted that the same physical description of air would hold if one reduced the number of such molecules to a sparse collection of only a few handfuls in a cubic inch container, or in a very small container. The conclusions are valid for all sized boxes as long as each side is significantly longer than the free flight length of 10^{-5} inch in normal air. It is that character of physics which will permit us to extend its scope to discussing more complex systems, such as living things, in which there are a great number of internal actions.

Equilibrium at the Macro Level

The key idea may now be stated: conditions inside the cubic inch are characterized and determined by the values of the conserved quantities. Two different cubic inches are macroscopically identical if they:

- contain the same matter content (defined as the number of molecules of each molecular type),
- the same momentum, and
- the same energy,

even though one is here now and the other was halfway round the globe a century ago. The reason is that the molecular players have the same properties in both cases:

- they interact the same way in both cases, and
- the large number of these stereotypic interactions (e.g., collisions) among the players results in standard distributions of each conserved quantity among the individual players, the distributions being the same in both cubic inches.

These standard distributions are called *equilibrium distributions*, and a small piece of the gas in which the equilibrium distribution is present is said to be in *local thermodynamic equilibrium*. Any deviation from the equilibrium distribution in a small piece is reduced very rapidly to zero by the stereotypical interactions inside the piece which act to share the conserved quantities among the players according to the equilibrium distribution. It is precisely this rapid drive toward local equilibrium that underlies the success and power of thermodynamics. Thermodynamics is the macrophysics within and between organized levels.

When the total momentum of a small piece (such

as our cubic inch) is zero, the piece is macroscopically at rest. When the total momentum is not zero, the piece is macroscopically in motion. The macroscopic velocity of the piece is equal to its momentum divided by its mass. Every small piece of still air is macroscopically at rest. Each small piece of windy air is in macroscopic motion, with different pieces generally moving with different velocities. What we have here is a *macroscopic flow field*.

The motional aspects of the situation illuminate the relation between the micro and macro levels of activity. The macroscopic velocity of a small piece is simply the directional (vector) average value of the velocities of all the microscopic players in the piece, each velocity being weighted by the mass of each player. Microscopically, there is a great deal of motion and action going on all the time even in a piece that is macroscopically at rest. The velocities of the individual players in such a piece have the standard equilibrium distribution. In a piece that is in macroscopic motion, the same equilibrium distribution of microscopic velocities is present, but in addition there is also the common macroscopic velocity. If such a piece is observed by an observer moving along with it, it appears identical to a piece that is macroscopically at rest.

Macroscopic Equation of State

The stereotypical interactions in a piece in local thermodynamic equilibrium give rise to a state of mechanical *stress* inside the piece. This stress is a mechanical measure of the intensity and frequency of the collisions taking place (the interactions that share the momentum among the players). The stress in a gas is called the *pressure*. It measures the average pressing force exerted (through collisions) by the players on one side of a square inch of area on the players on the other side of the same square inch. The pressure in a gas confined by a container is also the force exerted on each square inch of the container material (by collisions of the gas particles with the container walls).

Because the interactions share energy as well as momentum, there are also energy measures for the intensity of the local interactions. The direct measure is simply the energy per unit mass, or the energy per unit volume. A very important indirect, but more universal, measure is the *temperature*. Although temperature and the direct energy measure are closely related, the quantitative relation between them is different for different types of matter. Consider a macroscopically stationary piece of matter. When it is at its lowest possible temperature — absolute zero — it is at its lowest possible energy level, and its energy is called the *zero-point energy*. The energy of the piece increases as the temperature is raised. The excess of the energy above the zero-point energy is called the *thermal excitation energy*, or more simply, the *heat energy*. It is the heat energy that is distributed among the microscopic players according to the equilibrium distribution.

The temperature measure determines which way heat energy flows when two pieces of matter are placed in contact. Heat energy flows from higher to lower temperature. (When a finger at normal temperature contacts a hot stove, there is a flow of heat energy from stove to finger, causing it to get hotter and its owner to pull away).

The quantities that describe the macroscopic properties of a small macroscopic piece of a gas that is in local thermodynamic equilibrium are then:

- its matter content,
- its energy content,
- its temperature, and
- its pressure.

The matter content may be given by the *mass density* (mass per unit volume) and the *chemical composition* (the fractions of each of the chemical species making up the matter content). The energy content may similarly be given by the energy density. The macroscopic describers are sometimes called the *thermodynamic coordinates*.

Because the equilibrium distribution of momentum and energy among the players is completely determined by the matter content and energy content (by the actual physical account of local thermodynamic equilibrium), these two describers determine the values of the temperature and pressure. As a result, there is a functional relationship among the matter content, energy content, and temperature. This relation is called the *energy function*. There is also a functional relationship among the matter content, energy content, and pressure. Eliminating the energy content from these two functional relationships provides the function relating the matter content, temperature, and pressure. This relation may be called the *thermomechanical equation of state*.

Although the stereotypical motions of the individual players is different in detail for liquids as compared to gases, the main thermodynamic (macroscopic) conclusions are basically the same. In liquids, the individual molecules are very close to each other, just about touching, the distance determined by a near balance between the (long range) forces of attraction and the (short range) forces of repulsion. In fact, condensed matter – liquids and solids – form because of the forces of attraction.

One aspect of the stereotypical motion of the individual molecules in a liquid may be described as follows: Each molecule is confined by a 'cage' of surrounding molecules, all of them in thermal fluctuational motion. The caged molecule bounces back and forth with its cage for many cycles, until a fluctuation occurs which opens up a 'hole' in the surrounding cage, allowing the caged molecule to make a 'hop' to an adjoining location and a new cage. In a gas, the molecules make long flights separated by short quick changes in velocity. In a liquid, they make relatively short hops separated by many shorter back and forth bounces within their cage.

The end results are much the same, with the same set of macroscopic descriptors. The difference shows up in the details of the functional relations, the thermomechanical equation of state, and the energy function. (As an example, liquids are much more difficult to compress than gases).

Global Equilibria and Flow Motions

A complete macroscopic description of a flow field may be made by:

1) dividing the entire space into small elements of volume, and then
2) giving the thermodynamic coordinates and the macroscopic velocity of each small volume.

Such a description may be called a *hydrodynamical description.*

Consider a large body of fluid that is macroscopically at rest. If the net force on each of its volume elements is zero, then each volume element remains macroscopically at rest, and the fluid is said to be in *global mechanical equilibrium.* If the forces that act on the volume elements are not in balance, then the net force on each volume element sets it into motion. Friction between adjacent layers of fluid that slip past each other acts to stop the slipping and to bring the fluid back to rest in a new equilibrium state in which the forces are restored to balance. If the temperature is uniform throughout, the fluid is said to be in *global thermal equilibrium.* In this state, there is no flow of heat energy between adjacent volume elements. If the temperature is not uniform, heat energy flows through the fluid directed from high temperature places toward low temperature places. The flow is said to be 'down the temperature gradient', the path of greatest change with distance. The heat flow acts to equalize the regional temperatures, to drive the whole system toward global thermal equilibrium.

If the matter content is uniform in all volume elements, with uniform concentrations of each molecular species throughout the fluid, then there is no diffusional flow of any molecular species from element to element, and the fluid is said to be in *global chemical transport equilibrium*. If a concentration of any molecular species is not uniform, there is a *diffusional flow* of that species down the concentration gradient from high to low concentration places. This diffusional flow acts to equalize the concentrations, to drive the system toward global chemical transport equilibrium. (This brief discussion of chemical equilibrium neglects the effect of forces that act differently on different molecular species. Such forces can act to produce equilibrium situations in which some species are more concentrated in one location, and other species in other locations. This can occur by the action of electric forces on ionic species, and even by the gravity force which acts to concentrate denser species in locations of lower altitude. Also not considered as yet is the possibility of chemical transformations by chemical reactions, which introduces the idea of reaction equilibrium).

Global Thermodynamic Equilibrium

We have just examined the kinds of motion of flow that takes place in flow fields, and the three kinds of drives — mechanical, thermal, chemical — that are always acting to move the system toward global thermodynamic equilibrium. The state of global thermodynamic equilibrium is characterized by:

1) a balance of forces on every volume element and no macroscopic motion of matter,

2) uniform temperature throughout and no flow of heat energy,

3) uniform concentration of each chemical species (or a balance of special species forces) and no diffusional flow of any particular species.

The macroscopic motion induced by net forces is convective momentum flow. It is more simply called convective motion or **convection**. The momentum (and the associated macroscopic kinetic energy) is carried or conveyed by the moving fluid.

The heat energy flowing down the temperature gradient is a flow of heat energy through the fluid; the process is called *heat conduction*.

Similarly, the diffusional flow of a particular chemical species is also a flow through the fluid. Diffusional flow generally refers to relative motion of different chemical species within a volume element of a fluid. Two different chemical species can be diffusing in opposite directions

Finally, the friction force between adjacent layers of fluid that are slipping past each other is accomplished by a nonconvective momentum flow through the fluid, flowing from the higher speed fluid to the lower speed fluid. This process is called *viscosity*, more properly viscous diffusion.

To reiterate, macroscopic motion induced by net forces is called convection. In addition, there are three non-convective flows or transports that take place throughout the fluid:

1) heat conduction, or the transport of heat energy down temperature gradients,
2) diffusion flow, or the transport of particular chemical species down concentration gradients, and
3) viscosity, or the viscous momentum flow down slip-velocity gradients.

These three non-convective flows are the mechanisms of the drive toward global thermodynamic equilibrium. In an isolated system— one closed by fixed walls that prevent the exchange of matter and of energy between the system and outside—these mechanisms invariably and inexorably drive the system toward global equilibrium. The time scale for the approach to global equilibrium depends on the size of the system; but it is, in any case, a macroscopic time as compared to the short time scale for achieving the local equilibrium distributions within any small volume element.

Global Equilibrium Mechanisms

Although at first sight, the mechanisms of heat conduction, diffusion of chemical species, and viscosity appear to be different and independent, they all spring from the same process: the stereotypical fluctuational motion of the molecular players in the local equilibrium distribution.

To see this, focus attention on any imagined area inside a fluid. The molecules on each side of this area will, by virtue of their stereotypical fluctuational motions, do some crossing over to the other side of the area. This kind of 'diffusion mixing' across the common boundaries of adjacent volume elements acts to share and equalize the properties of the volume elements. If the fluid is hotter on one side of the area than the other, the diffusional mixing carries more energetic molecules into the hotter element, resulting in a transport of heat energy[5]. Similarly, if a particular chemical species is more concentrated on one side of the area than the other, the diffusional mixing accomplished by the fluctuational motions of these molecules results in a diffusion transport. Finally, if the macroscopic velocity is larger on one side of the area than the other, the diffusional mixing carries molecules with larger macroscopic velocity into the region of smaller macroscopic velocity, and carries molecules with smaller macroscopic velocity into the region of larger macroscopic velocity, resulting in a momentum transport down the velocity gradient.

The mechanisms of heat conduction, diffusional flow, and viscous momentum flow—the three one-way drives toward global thermodynamic equilibrium—all arise from the combined action of a macroscopic gradient (of temperature, concentration, or slip velocity) and the diffusional mixing generated by the local stereotypical fluctuation of the molecular players.

Examples of Macroscopic Action

Let us take a moment to look at the rich variety of processes that can occur in macroscopic flow fields. Firstly, consider some of the ways that forces are exerted on volume elements of the field matter. Forces

---

[5]EDITOR'S NOTE: It's been questioned whether Iberall meant "hotter element". We left it the way he wrote it.

may be exerted by external agents such as:

- the gravitational field of the Earth (this force is the weight of the volume element),
- an external electric or magnetic field (when the matter has appropriate electrical or magnetic properties),
- a variety of other agents such as fan blades or paddles.

Forces may also be exerted by a pressure gradient within the fluid itself, in which case a larger force is exerted on one side of a volume element than on the other side. The net pressure force on a volume element is directed down the pressure gradient, from high to lower pressure.

For a simple example, take a horizontal cylinder containing water confined between the closed end of the cylinder and a piston which is pushed against the water, thus pressurizing the water to a pressure that is higher than that of the surrounding atmosphere, 14.7 pounds per square inch, or psi. If a small hole is made in the closed end of the cylinder, the water will squirt out at high speed because the pressure exerted on each piece of water at the position of the hole is greater on the side facing the high pressure water than on the side facing the lower pressure air.

An example that involves two kinds of force is that of the atmosphere. Although the atmosphere is never macroscopically at rest, it is almost always fairly close to a balance of force on each of its volume elements. Small net forces result in large weather patterns. We may ask why the pressure at sea level is always fairly close to the value 14.7 psi. We may also ask why a piece of air that is located some distance above the ground or ocean does not fall down. After all, Earth attracts all matter with a gravity force. The answer to the first question is that a vertical column erected on one square inch of the Earth's surface and extending all the way up to extremely high altitudes, contains an amount of air that weighs 14.7 pounds. The atmosphere is pressurized by its own weight, by gravity force. The answer to the second question follows from the answer to the first. The pressure at each altitude is simply the weight of the air sitting above one square inch at that altitude, and consequently is greatest at sea level and decreases to zero at higher and higher altitudes. There is then a net upward pressure force exerted on each piece of air, called the *buoyant force*. The buoyant force is the excess of the upward directed pressure force exerted on its bottom face over the downward directed pressure force exerted on its top face. The upward buoyant force due to the pressure gradient balances the gravity force.

As a third example, consider an ordinary candle staying lit by the combustion of wax and oxygen at the tip of its wick. By its own action, the candle generates a steady supply of fresh oxygen-containing air (and a fresh supply of wax) at the wick tip. The heat generated by the chemical combustion process raises the temperature of the air in the flame cone. As a result, the air there expands, becomes less dense, and rises by buoyancy. As this air leaves by rising, the pressure is lowered causing surrounding air to be forced inward toward the burning place. The local heating leads to a continued flow of air inward from the surroundings and upward above the burning place. The candle generates this convection flow, ensuring a steady supply of fresh air. (At the same time, the heat of the flame melts the top of the candle, and molten wax climbs the wick—by capillary action—to the burning place. That capillary action represents the action of another force system which will not be explained here at this time. In any, case, again by its own action, the candle ensures a continued supply of wax at the burning place).

The candle process occurs in many forms in many places in nature. It initiates atmospheric motion on the Earth. Solar energy is absorbed mostly at sea level (ground level), resulting in heating of the air at sea level. This leads to convective rising and roiling motions in the atmosphere. Convective roiling in the Earth's mantle is initiated by the heat in the Earth's core and the radioactive heat produced in the mantle, and is responsible for the motion of the Earth's plates. The heat energy, generated in the core of the sun by (slow) nuclear fusion processes, is transported towards the surface first by heat conduction occurring via photons of light energy; but in the sun's outer half, the heat is carried to the surface by convective roiling where it is radiated out as sunshine.

Adding to the Earth processes already mentioned—gravity, solar heating from without and the roiling within—the spinning of the Earth (which affects the motion of the atmosphere, the oceans, and the fluid parts of the Earth's interior), the process of phase change (evaporation, condensation, cloud formation, rain, snow, glaciation, melting and freezing), capillary action, and the process of chemical transformation via chemical reaction, leads to the rich geophysical/geochemical/biochemical evolutionary history of planet Earth.

Study of flow field processes demonstrates that the diversity of macroscopic action at all scales of activity is always enhanced by diversity of structure (heterogeneity) at all scales, and by diversity of forces and energy supplies. (Even though the basic physical forces in nature are few, the diversification of their effects by the various ways they combine is rather enormous).

This is illustrated by a final simple example, that of a coffee percolator in which a repeated 'chug' cycle occurs because of the central tube of the percolator. When a pot of water without a central tube is heated from below, the heat is transferred to the entire body of water by convectional roiling, resulting in boiling throughout the water (phase change from water to steam within the water). In a coffee percolator, the central tube (with its flanged bottom) is too narrow to allow roiling inside it. As a result, the water at the bottom of the tube remains in place and is heated steadily to the boiling point at which time it quickly boils into steam and erupts upward in a geyser of hot water and steam—a chug. This eruption shakes the central tube causing it to lose contact with the bottom of the pot, and cooler water from outside the tube enters to be heated again to the boiling point leading to the next chug cycle.

Summary

Thermodynamics is used to study the interactions

Thermodynamics

between large ensembles of objects. Three types of drives — mechanical, thermal, and chemical — are always acting to move a system towards global thermodynamic equilibrium. This state is characterized by a balance of forces, uniform temperature, and uniform concentration of each chemical species. The mechanisms that drive a system toward global thermodynamic equilibrium are three non-convective flows: heat conduction, diffusion flow, and viscous momentum flow. All three spring from the stereotypical fluctuational motion of particles in the local equilibrium distribution. An ordinary candle uses convection flow to ensure a steady supply of fresh air to fuel the fire, using the change in air temperature and pressure to create a flow field. This same process is seen in atmospheric motion and roiling in the Earth's mantle. The study of flow field processes demonstrates that the diversity of macroscopic action at all scales of activity is always enhanced by diversity of structure, forces, and energy supplies.

LESSON 4
THE PHYSICS OF COMPLEX SYSTEMS[6]

The fundamental principle that makes physics the first and only science is and remains this: the field process of atomistic interactions in any physical field can only involve pair by pair conservations. In Lesson 2, we looked at where the conservations of motion and change come from. We started with the simplest kinds of atomisms colliding—a pair of "balls" banging into each other. These could be, for example, molecular or atomic "balls." As well, they could be baseballs, billiard balls, golf balls, ping-pong balls, gum balls, sand particles, or dust particles. We then discussed what happens in terms of mass, momentum, and energy conservations from the pair

---

[6]Revised from *The physics of complex systems, CP2: Commentaries – Physical and Philosophic Vol. 1. No. 2 Society 1.2, 1990* and from *A Course of Study on Homeokinetics: The Physics of Complex Systems: Introduction, Bulletin 1, 1997*

by pair collisions. However, there is a problem, in that we have to face the fact that there are different kinds of pair by pair interactions.

In a simple exercise, we'll describe about eight different kinds of "balls" bouncing into each other, and, each time, provide an atomistic case, simple or complex, in which the physical process can be seen.

Case 1: Symmetrically Conservative Interactions

A ball bounces and hits something such as a wall. It then bounces back as high or as fast as it was thrown. This example, called a "symmetrically conservative" interaction, follows the common idea that most people have regarding collisions, in that you can't tell the difference if the collision took place "backward" or "forward". Perhaps A bounces into B and they bounce out in different states of motion A' and B'. Or the reverse takes place, where A' and B' bounce into each other, producing states A and B.

We see this in bouncing balls, projectiles hurled through space, planetary "balls" moving around each other attracted by gravitational force.

The word "conservative" here means that the interaction is *conservative and reversibly mechanical*. This is in distinction to the rest of the cases which we will see will be irreversibly thermodynamic (see below).

Can you see such continuing motion as reversible conservative interactions seem to imply? Certainly. As we saw in Lesson 2, fill up a glass of water, blow up a balloon, or put rocks in a tub. What happens among them? The balls, atomic or molecular balls, are indefinitely bouncing on each other. Put them in a container with a certain temperature and they keep bouncing indefinitely. They also will create the return momentum of pressure as they bounce against any or all confining walls.

To discuss this issue, Maxwell introduced the physical study of a kinetic theory of matter, a statistical mechanics of matter. Writing an article in 1860, he said, "So many of the properties of matter, especially when in gaseous form, can be deduced from the hypothesis that their minute [very small] parts are in rapid motion...that the precise nature of their motion becomes a subject of rational curiosity."

Case 2: Frictional Loss of Energy

A ball bounces, but it does not bounce as high or as fast as from whence it was started or dropped[7]. You can try it by dropping a real ball on any good hard surface and you will see such loss of height and energy. The energy is not conserved at the bouncing level; thus, the motion is not reversible. We say that there was **a frictional loss of energy**. That "lost" energy went into heat: the ball or what it bounced against got a little warmer.

This interaction is not reversibly mechanical. Thus, it is *irreversibly thermodynamic*. Irreversibly thermodynamic means that energy will persist but not at the same level as in the simpler mechanically interacting balls; it will go out to other lower levels of

---

[7]This is looking at the problem as half a system. We can imagine one ball bouncing against another identical ball. One ball bouncing against an impervious immovable wall makes up a half system.

organization. The first law of thermodynamics, which comes from pure mechanics, states that regardless of how the balls bounce, energy cannot be lost, only transformed into other forms or levels. According to the second law, energy will be transformed into lower levels of organization as a result of natural processes. This law is important for irreversible thermodynamics.

Let us talk about how this second case is different yet also the same as the first case. Can you do this process with a bunch of balls? Certainly. Put a bunch of fine particles—sand, pills, Wheaties, or diatomaceous earth—in a box and shake it. You can even see or hear the particles bouncing around on each other. But, differing from the first case, in time they stop. Why? Because of friction in their encounters. Due to the thermodynamics of their motion rather than the mechanics of bouncing, they lose energy into heat on each bounce and ultimately stop bouncing. If you want to see these particles exhibit indefinite motion as in the first case, put vibrators or buzzers on the walls of the container. That vibration will restore movement to the ensemble. Particles resting at the walls will be impulsed into motion.

Think of this as baseball. The "batters" at the wall will keep making "base hits." Once out in the field, they share their motion via impulses, and the batters at the wall soon get all the players out in the field back into motion. In time, all that vibrational energy imparted at the walls gets shared or partitioned out in the field. This is called "equipartitioning of the energy."

In the first case, the molecules have "sustained motion." While not immediately obvious, their energy came from the sustained temperature of the walls. Something was maintaining the wall temperature. To put this another way, vibrational energy was put into the molecules in the wall which happen to be bound together into a solid form. (We have been only looking at fluid motions in the ensemble, but let us mention that these molecules in the solid state are bound together physically-chemically as or by springs. Think of a solid form like the application of a solid bat, which brooks no nonsense from a ball pitched at it.) In baseball terms, think of the wall as being many batters. One or more of the batters in the wall will always make a hit. Imagine a poor pitcher, faced not by one batter, but by a dense myriad of batters, all swinging away or even picking balls off the ground, tossing them up and hitting them into play. Vibrating the walls by putting an electric buzzer on them simulates temperature. The sand or dust particles will move and sustain the play.

To see why this second case simulates the first case, let's take the first container of gas molecules outside into the cold. The wall temperature will lower. We'll find that the molecules do not possess as much motional energy as before. Their temperature — meaning their energetic motion governed by the walls — is less. The two cases are almost the same.

If you tried the second case experiment with very fine dust particles, you would find that the particles stay in sustained motion a very long time, if not indefinitely. By looking under a microscope, you can even see the motion. This type of motion was noted in 1827 by Robert Brown, a Scottish botanist who observed under a microscope the movement of plant spores floating in water. Albert Einstein proved that the motion of those fine particles—which are very much larger than atoms and molecules—have their motion supported, as Brownian motion, from the impulses of the very much smaller molecules and their molecular motions. Think of them as very small impulsing batters. Their motion is also supported by impulses from the vibrating energy of the walls. Brownian motion is directly supported by molecular motion coming from the walls.

In actuality, this is not quite true. If we reduce the wall temperature to lower and lower temperatures, toward what is called the absolute zero of temperature, we find that all motion does not cease. Ways to get toward that temperature are using: a water ice bath (0°C), a solid carbon dioxide bath (-79°C), a liquid nitrogen bath (-196°C), or a liquid helium bath (-268°C). A theory says you cannot get lower than -272.15°C which is very near 0°K. People have produced baths within 0.001°C of absolute zero of absolute temperature and are moving toward one millionth of a °C of it. This concept of absolute zero temperature is actually more than a concept, it is a very real number and state. For example, the average temperature throughout the reach of the universe, away from hot stars and gases, is about -268°C, near liquid helium temperature.

As you go down in wall temperature, you might expect all molecular motion to cease. But physicists discovered a newer branch of mechanics, more elaborate than Newtonian mechanics, called *quantum mechanics*. There is a small measure, known as *Planck's constant h*, which can serve to do what temperature does at very small motional energy levels. The constant h can substitute as a source of action, thus producing the equivalent of a small temperature motion. In order to look at how much motion, we need to discuss how much equivalent temperature can be produced by h. This formula will help:

$$h/t = hf = kT$$

where:

kT is the motional energy associated with temperature T
f = frequency
t = period of vibration ($t = 1/f$)

The formula tells us how much equivalent temperature T can be produced by h if the effect of h is to create a process cycle, or a vibration, with the period of vibration t (or of the frequency f, so many jitters per second). If h were zero, then we would be in a Newtonian world. But since it is not, we are in a mixed Newtonian-quantum mechanical world. The part that Newton did not explore was that part which becomes involved in the connections between quantum mechanics and thermodynamics. You cannot ignore all quantum theory when you want to manage real systems.

In the end, it is quantum effects at the level of h

which relate and sustain the bottom motion of small fundamental entities and their essential interactions with the physical vacuum. This is why, when not in an arena of very small size or very low temperature where quantum effects must be accounted for, the two cases of motion — conservative and frictional — are very much alike.

The Brownian motion example permits us to bridge the micro-macro gap. When you go out into the sunlight, not only do you get the thermal motion of all the atoms, molecules, and photons[8], but you get the energy of all Brownian particles among these particles. You also get the energy that other Brownian particles are able to extract both physically and chemically from those particles. These latter could include, for example, small living cells. That process works its way through all levels up to the point even when you reach into your cupboard and take out some bagels and lox and eat them. You also are a Brownian creature, even though you're big. The whole process is a Great Chain of Being (and Becoming, and, eventually, Unbecoming).

Case 3: Stickiness

A ball bounces on another ball or hard surface and

---

[8]Photons have no mass, they only have hf where f is their vibratory frequency; they can collide and share and equipartition energy. They also can show a similar equation of state, including temperature and pressure. It is easy to show that photons — in effect, light beams — exert pressure. Why else do you think that those little particles stay floating around indefinitely wherever you look?

it sticks. You can try this with putty or asphalt in order to see the process. (You can also get married.)

Case 4: Deformation

A ball bounces on another ball or hard surface, and one or the other deform. Try dropping a piece of fruit, or any other squishy thing, even, say, a block of wood and watch it dent.

Case 5: Breaking

A ball bounces on another ball, and one or the other cracks or splinters into pieces. Try a glass ball on a hard metal surface.

Case 6: Exchanging of Bonds

A ball (particle, atomism) bounces on another ball (particle, atomism). One or both break up and some or all of the pieces rejoin. This chemical reaction takes place in your stomach when you eat a cookie. It takes place in a glass of water when you put an Alka Seltzer in it and watch a fizzing chemical reaction. Put some yeast in dough and watch a reaction take place as the dough rises. Or breathe in and out—in comes the good air (oxygen), out goes the bad (carbon dioxide). Or burn a piece of paper, or gasoline, or gas. You've conducted a chemical reaction.

Just to give you a flavor of writing a chemical reaction, namely identifying what all the atoms and molecules are doing, we will write verbally the oxidative reaction that supplies energy to our bodies. It is one of a number of thermodynamic processes that make life possible:

- fuel + oxygen → carbon dioxide + water + byproducts

→ is a symbol that means goes to form. Or, since we use a variety of fuels:

- simple carbohydrate + oxygen → carbon dioxide + water
- protein + oxygen → carbon dioxide + water + byproducts (among the byproducts, for example, are urea which appears in our urine)
- oils or fats + oxygen → carbon dioxide + water + byproducts (among those byproducts are acetone, which at times can be smelled on your breath)

The oxygen on the left-hand side of the equation comes in through your lungs when you breathe, or comes in through your gills from the surrounding water if you are a fish. The carbon dioxide and water on the right-hand side may go out through your breath or your urine.

From this beginning at the notions of chemistry, note that the social machinery within you or that you manage has to deal with both sides of the reaction— both for providing supplies for intake and the management of outgoes, whether directly useful to your system or not. If you don't manage both sides, the system can easily come to a halt.

Of course, you should understand that your body is also working on other reactions, for example, anabolic reactions— ones that build up your tissue:

- carbohydrates + fats + some proteins + oxygen → your proteins + carbon dioxide + water + byproducts

There is also a large family of cells that are not aerobic, that do not use oxygen in their metabolism. They are generally considered to be primitive but they are perfectly competent in their capability to persist and coexist with your oxygenators.

Case 7: Pair Annihilation and Pair Production

Two bodies collide and they both disappear, producing only an equivalent remnant energy of photons. Equally astounding, a bolt of photonic energy strikes a point and out comes two bodies! This process is known as *pair annihilation* and *pair production*. It only happens with elementary particles—electrons, protons, neutrons, and many other fundamental particles (which, ultimately, are all elementary combinations of a few leptons and quarks). Briefly, they require a rather complete quantum theory, involving that little number h, the minimum quantum of action, and also Einstein's derivation from special relativity, $E_o = mc^2$. Physics also has a large number c—the velocity of light. It turns out that mass m can be converted into energy E_o (from that mass at rest) according to this measure c, but that can only take place with very small particles when they are moving very fast. It is that kind of nuclear reaction that makes stars burn and give off energy, as well as make atom bombs and nuclear reactors work. It was that energy from the sun that made planetary processes possible, including the process of life. These processes in the stars also made all the matter we deal with, except for some more primordial matter like hydrogen and helium. Knowing these elaborate processes will help one manage whole Earth systems if that is one's desire. Life comes as the result of very energetic collisions of particles. It emerges both as an evolutionary and a developmental process.

Case 8: More Particles

One last interaction: two particles collide and after some delay, a bunch of little particles come out from the collision. This is the process of sexual intercourse and reproduction.

From these examples, you see the physics of pair interaction is very rich. It is worthwhile to carry that rich picture with you every time to want to start in on the management of a different physical system. Each time, you will be dealing with the pair by pair collisions and their conservations.

Atomisms in Simple Systems

Atomisms, whether simple or complex, sustain their motion by interacting with walls and other depots that supply their fundamental conservations. All such depots are called *potentials* or *potential stores*. Thus, like simple atomistic systems, complex atomisms may get:

- temperature or energy of motion from the walls

- momentum—either as a diffusive influx or convectively as from a stream—from or through the walls
- chemical potentials (storage of various mass species) from or through the walls or in depots distributed throughout the field space

Still only viewing them as simple systems, we turn to some of the *internal characteristics of the atomisms* (or molecularities). A *molecularity* is a bound form of a number of atomisms, for example, the binding of two people in a partnership or a number of people in a company.

In Lesson 3, when we spoke of the energy of motion of a particle (its kinetic energy), we did not indicate that such a characterization meant that our particle was likely a rigid solid-like particle. The six degrees of motional freedom were motions of translation (side to side movements) in three spatial directions—such as N-S, E-W, and up-down—and motions of rotation in three directions of spin. These did not exhaust all possible degrees of freedom and we even named where some of the others might come from. But we didn't indicate that those six degrees were "external" degrees of freedom. Now we have to clarify "internal" degrees of freedom (ones inside the atomisms).

1. *We can store energy internally as springy motion.* During the same period of time that Newton laid down the laws of motion and

talked about the universal law of gravity[9], another physicist, Sir Robert Hooke (1635-1703), discovered another basis for mechanical force. That force on matter, he said, measured by the push or pull on any chunk of matter, causes a "movement" or "displacement" in the direction of the force which is proportional to the force. Hooke had discovered a source for an internalized process in matter — the *elastic* or *spring force*[10].

Blow gas into a balloon. Feel the elasticity of the gas (but separate this from that of the balloon; the balloon has its own elasticity which can be tested by blowing up a paper bag or sack instead). Stretch a rubber band or bend a steel rod; you can feel their elasticity. Press on water (by doing a belly flop into a pool); you can feel its elasticity. The water's elasticity is better seen if you press on it with a heavy duty hydraulic pump. Freeze a bottle of water or wine in your refrigerator, and see the water or wine expand and push as it freezes. You will see that each phase of matter has a different measure of elasticity: solids are stiffest, liquids next, and gases the least stiff (or, conversely,

---

[9]Gravitational force is a mechanical force system whereby all particles of matter attract or tend to move in toward each other in proportion to their respective masses.

[10]The elastic force is not a primary force. Each of the primary forces, such as gravity or the electric force, can produce spring force.

gases are the most compressible and solids the least).

Exerting a force through a distance changes the energy in the system and does work. This new form of energy is referred to as the *internal potential energy.* It lies within the atomism either in interior motions of part of the atomism or else it lies in the field. For the former, it can be, for example, vibrations or rotations of parts. For the latter, we will show it to you in a couple of ways.

When you lift up a body in the Earth's gravitational field—pick up a stone, for example—you become aware that a force is required on your part to overcome the force of the gravity by which a very big Earth attracts that stone. (If you try lifting a stone on the Moon, you would find it requires a much smaller force. This is because the mass of the Moon, which is doing the attraction, is so much less than the Earth's.) You did work in lifting that stone. Does that increase of energy remain in the system? Certainly. Drop the stone to the level from which you lifted it or onto your foot and see how that recovered energy—now an energy of motion—can do work, for example, in crushing your foot. Where was that energy when you lifted the stone? It is in the field. (Einstein elaborated that into a very strange and marvelous descriptive form of physics: general relativity.)

2. *Electrical charge is another internalized property of matter that "creates" a force in a*

sense similar to gravity. Electrical charge can develop either a push or a pull. There are so-called "plus" or "minus" charges. Electrical charges that are alike, such as two "plus" charges, push apart. Unlike charges, such as a plus and minus pair, pull together. This process allows an electrical force to conduct through rods, wires, even through the muscle fibers in our bodies. In fact, what we ordinarily call pushes and pulls is most commonly due to very close, very intimate electrical forces even if it doesn't seem so and the process appears hidden from us. It is hidden because the electrical charges reside in the very small atoms.

3. *Nuclear forces are a few even more intimate forces.* However, these are beyond the scope of this work but we mention them because they are just another example.

   To summarize, we can see energy stored in kinetic forms of motion—either external or internal—and in potential forms internal to the field. (There is the third way of converting mass into energy, such as between photons and fundamental matter particles, but that only takes place under very very strong forces, so we can ordinarily neglect those processes. We see them, as we said, in how our sun and other stars generate energy, and we see it in certain atoms that are radioactive and unstable, such as radium and uranium).

4. *A simple mass particle might have up to 12 degrees of freedom into which it could store*

energy. It may store kinetic energy of motion stored in each of its 3 degrees of "translational" freedom or 3 degrees of "rotational" freedom. It might have spring or potential storage stored in them. That would be the specific heat (or energy) you could find in an elastic ball-like atomism or molecularity. Each degree of temperature that you heat up such a ball — transferring energy into the ball — requires that you put energy into those 12 modes of motion.

5. **Energy can be associated with fragments of a molecularity.** This occurs in chemical change. If you put enough heat energy into a molecularity, it may break an elastic bond and you would see fragmented particles. Or, conversely, particles may join up and give up a binding energy and stay tied by a spring-like bond. For example, to get married — to come together in the partnership bonds of matrimony — means to give up an energy given to the act of bonding.

In simple atomic chemistry, we will not be concerned with annihilation and pair production of matter. We will have to be concerned with the additional conservation of electrical charges — of their plus and minus forms and of their total or net amounts, but we are not going to provide a great deal of detail about the electrical processes except to point out that they exist. We will also point out that the two force systems — the gravity force and the electrical force — are effectively the two forces that we see acting to organize things around us. The other two forces (strong and weak nuclear forces) tend to act intimately at the very very small size of things within us and all around us, but that is all bottom line physics.

To summarize, with simple systems:

- We see the pair by pair conservations of a) mass, b) momentum, and c) energy; there is also the other conservation of d) electrical charge to consider.
- If our field systems are made up of atomisms whose electrical charges are paired up, plus and minus — then we consider them electrically neutral molecularities. Metaphorically speaking, they have gotten married and finished "sparking", so that they do not play electrical games anymore (at least not in public!).
- Simple system equations of state are in terms of these three or four physical conservations. Also, corresponding to each conservation, there is an equation of change for the dynamic field.

In addition, if the banging particles bang together sufficiently energetically to break up the plus-minus electrical bonds, then the fragments may continue to form and to rejoin up in combinations until only certain pairings will continue to persist. Such a conglomerate field is known as a field in *chemical or near chemical equilibrium*: as many players are transforming in one direction as in the other direction. Such kinds of processes are viewed as *dynamic equilibria.* If the processes of change continue, you can have a mixture of atoms, molecules (which are combinations of atoms), and ions[11]. The latter are electrically charged fragments, made by uneven separation of plus-minus particles. If this pairing, breaking, and bonding (i.e., chemistry) occurs — a result of the particles' electrical nature — there are equations of state for each mass species that continue to exist.

Atomisms in Complex Systems

We saw that in simple systems, when the atomisms bang into each other, their internal interactions are like those of simple springs. In a few interactive collisions, they are brought to equilibrium. When complex atomisms (or molecularities) bang into each other, their internal interactions are different. Instead, their internal movements are never brought to a simple state of completion within one or a few interactive collisions. Their interior movements are organized into very very long time delayed patterns as countable by external bangings. We have estimated that in complex field systems, the time for internal patterns to settle down is of the order of 10,000 bangings minimally, and in the cases that really are

---

[11]Atoms consist of electrically charged electrons (minus charge) circling a nucleus with plus charge, where the two sets of charge are equal in number. Ions are atoms that are unbalanced so that the two sets of charge are no longer the same: they may have too many or too few electrons. Think of it as humans trying to find opposite electrical partners to marry. This continuing motion of chemical bonding represents an additional diffusive transport. That transport into specific atoms and molecules is called the **chemical reaction rate.**

going to interest us, in the order of millions, billions, or trillions of bangings. This by itself may help you understand that the physics of complex atomisms is quite different from the physics of simple atomisms. There is a lot of internal 'hanky-panky' going on.

Complex systems still involve movement and change. The atoms and molecules still remain the same kind of ball players. But what is different is the *long time delayed internal processes* that are taking place. What are they? They comprise a factory of processes which are, for the most part, long drawn out flow processes. The players are the same kind as before but they are involved also in much slower play. Most commonly, this is due to very long and large associations between the players. *They play weaker or slower games on top of their fast games.* They involve remnant weak components of strong forces. We say that they are involved in a complex "cascade" of energetic processes pouring into and through the field system at very many time and process scales.

Let's state this another way. The processes of change they engage in internally are so slow that it looks as if they had a memory. No "story" of what a complex system is engaged in can be described from the outside in a completed form in one or a few interactions. It goes on through an interminable number of external interactions before even the simplest of their "stories" are complete. The great mathematician-physicist, John von Neumann, grasped this idea when he provided the modern digital computer with a temporary memory storage in the form of a standing wave on a liquid. He possibly got the clue for this from a dear friend, the neurophysiologist Warren McCulloch. This is not different from you tying a knot on your finger where the persistent wave of excitation of your nervous system continues to remind you of something that you want to remember.

Let us imagine wandering around inside a big molecule, a cell, your body, a city, a civilization, or a galaxy. It will always look like a giant busy play. All you will see are pieces moving in and out of a great number of stations; activities and processes are continually going on. It isn't until a great number of steps have taken place at some or all stations that what is going to emerge becomes apparent as a "product" or a "message"; i.e., that you know that Act I of the play has taken place, or that an inning has been played. What emerges from the material-energetic transformations are only such higher ordered "products" or "messages" made up of the same kind of material-energetic processes we see in the simplest of systems. We add one more transporting diffusion: a diffusion into internal action. That diffusion measure is called the *associational viscosity*. Here is where the long time delay lies which makes for complexity.

We can answer briefly two questions: why can we call it "physics"; and what does that get us? It is physics because, once again, we can identify new conservations and how the processes of association take place and what they represent. That gives us the chance to use the same science we used before for the simpler systems. Why is that good or necessary? Because, as we said, there is only one science. To put it more precisely, there is either only one science or there are no sciences.

We are fortunate that the physical game played by nature is and has to be indefinitely repetitious. It is only because of that that we can deal with the many forms of those games by attempting to recognize the repetitions. We can deal with the physics of complex systems because we can recognize their conservations. Otherwise, we could not deal with them scientifically. The thing that makes our game not a tautology is that complex systems exist, and we can find their conservations by the rules of physics. They arise from the forces that nature exhibits and uses. The physics we are describing is only possible for games that persist in nature. Other, non-persistent, systems may pass before our eyes. Perhaps we can talk about their kinetics. We cannot fully talk about them as field systems. It is only a complex system if the complex patterns it displays repeat again and again and again. It is like a play that repeats again and again with only moderate changes in its patterns. It is baseball played in myriads of ball parks for interminable innings.

Factory Day of Complex Systems

If, as we perhaps might or might not suspect, we are in one universe, we cannot be certain of what came before all the yesterdays of time before "today" and we cannot be certain of what will be all of the tomorrows. So we are not yet fully certain about the entire system of our universe. Since the messages or products are not complete in one particle or atomism interaction, what do we do about conservations?

Where are they?

They emerge from the *"factory day."* This is a much longer period of time over which all of the internal associations take place within the complex atoms. And then that day is repeated. How do we know that such a factory day exists? We only know when we can see it and find it.

If you have billions of billions of billions of stars and you look at them and you see a pattern of stages — of birth, middle age, and death among them — and you figure out such is the process that is going on among them, then you can grasp the factory day of their performance. Their factory day may be a million to a hundred billions of years. Astronomers studying stars over many, many nights get a notion of the physical processes by which stars sustain their field existence. Biologists can do the same for millions of living organisms today; paleontologists for millions of species of organisms in the past.

Physicists have begun to do that analysis for galaxies, stars, planetary and planetesimal bodies, living organisms, for chemical, geochemical, biochemical, and nuclear chemical processes, and for atoms, ions, and molecules. My colleagues and I have begun to indicate what such "star charts" would show for living societies. The theme and its variations are not new. Using these laws of physics, it is possible to figure out the factory day for most systems. Let us explore in the next sections what such a factory day is like for a human organism.

Factory Day for Human Organisms

At a first rudimentary level, one takes a breath. Then one takes another breath, and so on and on. As long as breath follows breath, and heart beat follows heart beat, some of the fundamental internal machinery is working. Note that the process starts out of the momentum and the movements of the heart, the lungs, and the other organs. At the bottom of this, there still remains only momentum, energy, matter, and electric charge.

But let us jump to a more integrative level. There is more to see over the day. Besides keeping its heart beating and lungs breathing, the organism has searched for and acquired food, slept, moved, drunk fluids, voided, and interpersonally interacted with its fellow organisms. There is much more machinery involved at this level. But notice, more or less, one day is like another.

This is still not quite integrative enough. There are other machinery processes, such as water balance over three days and the female menstruation cycle which involves the chemical apparatus associated with sex and reproduction. But engraved within the body's machinery there is more nearly a yearly scaling of processes. That may be seen in the reproductive balance, in dealing with the seasons by the body machinery. The factory day for us as individuals is one or a few days or hardly more than one year.

Factory Days for Species and Life

There is also the striking balances with other species making up the trophic web of life. The squirrel eats and stores nuts; we eat the squirrel; the worms eat us; the bacteria eat the worms; they put the matter stuff back into the rivers and oceans and earth and atmosphere; and the plant eats from these and grows the nuts seasonally or longer. All this goes on, with many threads in process, in space, in time.

At a still more integrative level, sexual organisms reproduce themselves, roughly in a generation time, many in even longer periods. Our human generation time is approximately 20-30 years; we live perhaps close to three generations. This becomes developmental. It becomes the factory day for our species. In comparison to the factory day of the stars, the one for our species is hardly longer than the one for us as individuals.

Beyond that lie longer scales even more integrative, with a factory day for life as a whole — for all species — beginning perhaps 3.8 billion years ago, not too long after the birth of our planet. This scale is evolutionary.

You now can see many factory days, each one or level has to be attended to by its physics, by its conservations. In toto, as one runs through the entire gamut of such factory days, one finds an entire cascade spectrum of energetic processes. Energy flows through, transforms level to level.

Conservations of Complex Systems

Energy. The conservations of complex systems are the simple conservations transformed a bit. Energy and flow of energy through the atomistic states remains energy and the flow of energy. But we have discussed that there are internal ways to store that energy. In particular, in complex systems, there is a characteristic energy which is stored in the atomism and there is a characteristic factory day flow of energy passing through the atomistic system. For example, in the human organism, the characteristic energy stored in that organism is about 600,000 kilocalories, or kcal, of energy, the amount of energy that you might find stored and available to burn in about 300 lbs. of sugar. (The Nazi experiments performed on people "proved" that that is what you could get out of a person by working him or her to death). We can see it when we put on or take off pounds at a caloric cost of about 3,500 kcal per pound. The characteristic factory day energy when the Earth day is taken to be the factory day, is about 2,000 kcal per Earth day (perhaps 1,800 for adult females, 2,400 for adult males).

Mass. There is a characteristic mass and distribution of mass species, and a characteristic flow of a variety of mass species per factory day in the organism. In simple systems, it was perhaps one or a few mass species. In living organisms, those mass species are carbohydrates, oils or fats, proteins, water, some ions, some salts and minerals, modest amounts or traces of some heavy metals, e.g. iron, magnesium, selenium, molybdenum. The chemistry in the human corresponds as a rough average to 130 lbs. of ingredients and to the factory day flow of those ingredients which will burn (oxidize) in net and produce 2,000 kcal each factory day. What is that material flow? A little more than 1/2 lb. of carbohydrate, 2 oz. of fat, 2 oz. of protein, a quart or two of water, and a pound of oxygen each day. The byproducts emerge as carbon dioxide, urine (some water and byproducts like urea) and feces (with a considerable fraction of undigested materials and dead bacteria who lived high off "the hog" in passage through your GI tract).

Momentum. Momentum—the result of the pair by pair collisions representing forces which change momentum—is transformed in complex systems into *action* that emerges from the complex factory day of the rapidly colliding atomisms. Action is the energy-time product. What emerges is their organized actions rather than the itsy-bitsy changes in momentum from collisions at simpler levels. From cells banging into cells, we see their complex slower biochemistry emerging; from that system level, we see organized actions throughout the organs; from thence we see the organized actions of the organism; from them we see the organized actions of the social group. We should recognize most of these actions as trans-actions. Each level is made up of the organized momentum-like characteristics of lower atomistic processes. That is all there is.

To state this in physics, we could say: The sum of all of the small momentum changes taking place at every level throughout the organism over the factory day represents a *characteristic daily action* H_o which itself is the summation of a spectrum or matrix of daily actions.

If human organisms were simple fundamental particles, their simple "factory day" of interaction (their collision scale) would be h or a few times that number. That was the marvel of quantum mechanics. But humans have H_o which is characteristic of the species. The daily action of a human is the same 2,000 kcal of energy expended during the factory day, but also 2,000 kcal-days of action. That is what you, as the organism, ate and ingested material and energy for, so that you could perform that characteristic action. And what characteristic daily actions did you do with that characteristic daily energy? You ate, slept, worked, voided, got mad, made love, attended to people, got envious, got anxious, escaped, played, etc. We can begin to recognize the human drama. How do you know a person, or any other living creature? By observing them and noting their characteristic spectrum or stream of action, the transactions they engage in. In fact, you can furnish a list and know that, somewhere on Earth, anything you put down on the list someone is doing — today, and yesterday, and tomorrow. It is both a glorious, objective, and a disgusting thought, but that's it.

In summary, the conservational transactions for complex atomisms are:

- factory day fluxes or streams of characteristic energy,
- characteristic mass species, and
- a spectrum of characteristic actions that make up the equation of state and equations of change of the species ensemble and their play.

Other Measures

Let us look at what happens in complex systems regarding mass density, temperature, and pressure.

Mass density. Mass density, still an overall simple concept, now has all of its component specific mass or number densities of each independent or chemically transforming atomism.

Temperature. Temperature, still measurable as

kinetic energy of motion in any external motional degree of freedom (for example, how much energy or action you expend in eating), is elaborated into the specific energy via all of the channels into which energy can be stored — all the other motions and potentials stored in the field space.

Pressure. Pressure, deriving from momentum, itself can no longer be perceived as a simple measure. As we went from a simple gas phase with momentum representing the changes in motion for sharply distinguishable collisions, we reached the still relatively simple liquid phase with momentum now also representing the associated state of many close neighbors hammering (and yammering) at each other. We begin to notice that the pressure now is elaborated by the close field forces of attraction and repulsion between the players (where these forces are most commonly electrical). But when we come to complex atomisms, their associations display a resulting new transport from their interiors — their associational viscosity. As well, their internal actions, the form of the energies that pour out from their interiors, affect the partitioning of the external momentum. And so we see a new process in the pressure. We see the *social pressure* of the associated complex ensemble.

We will give you a metaphor, what the music sounds like when one strikes a note in a complex system. If you are a simple system and we give you a push, you bounce away. If you are a complex atomism, you may still bounce away but three weeks later you continue to wonder why we did it! The melody lingers on. And for all we know, you may then hit us. In another example, if you see two players join in a simple system, you know a simple chemical bond formed. In a complex ensemble, you do not know whether they conspired to kill the king, decided to form a company, make love, or were just trying to find directions to a restroom or the First National Bank. That complex of internal associations and its externalization defines the social pressure. Where does it come from? Still from the simple internal forces and processes, electrical and chemical flow, say at the brain organ, but it is hierarchical chemistry now, it is a complex of processes and internal flows.

Language as Catalyst

One last property of that transformed action complex that emerged from simple momentum and forces is the transport of action and the switching of actions associated with "information" and "language." In fact, we define *language* as the small matter-energy catalysts that switch or evoke states of action.

Language is physical. Whether we whisper to someone using an acoustic signal or an electrical signal, or wave using a chemical signal such as a perfume or pheromones, or make a mechanical signal, we are using a small matter-energy complex. Language is a catalyst because its action is only to amplify and change some other system's motion without itself being affected. And its effect, as that kind of amplifier, is to get your action attention and/or to evoke in you a new action state. All this is the real working part of the social pressure in complex system. Someone can say, "Conquer the enemy for God and country!" and use that language to convince others to hurl themselves into action. Or someone can say, "Let's loot" or "Let's lynch," and civil unrest occurs. Or "Let's stay home, it's raining" can be equally compelling. (Think how small the energy is that is represented by the putting of this writing in ink on the paper as compared to what that energy might release in action if you take us seriously.)

A memory function of a physical-chemical nature makes possible the use of language to make possible the long time delay in action in the factory day of a complex atomism.

And we need only add one idea to the prescription of equations of state and change. We have to continue to identify the potentials that drive such a field system or ensemble of players. Those potentials still arise from the walls or distributed depots. The potentials themselves may either be simple or complex systems. But they still provide energy, matter densities, momenta or sources that supply, govern, or evoke action.

Summary

As defined in our *Science* article (see appendix), a system is a collective of interacting atomistic-like entities. We use the word atomism to stand both for the entity and the doctrine. As is known from kinetic theory, in mobile or simple systems, the atomisms share their energy in interactive collisions. That so-called equipartitioning process takes place within a few collisions. Physically, if there is little or no interaction, the process is considered to be very weak.

Physics deals basically with the (few) forces of interaction that influence the interactions. They all tend to emerge with considerable force at high density of atomistic interaction.

In complex systems, there is also a result of internal processes in the atomisms. They exhibit, in addition to the pair-by-pair interactions, internal actions such as vibrations, rotations, and association. If the energy and time involved internally creates a very large—in time—cycle of performance of their actions compared to their pair interactions, we say that the collective system is *complex*. If you eat a cookie and you do not see the resulting action for hours, that is complex; if boy meets girl and they become engaged for a protracted period, that is complex. What emerges out of that physics is a broad host of changes in state and stability transitions in state. Namely, in our opinion, if we view Aristotle as having defined a general basis for systems in their static-logical states and tried to identify a logic-metalogic for physics (e.g., metaphysics), we view homeokinetics to be an attempt to define the dynamics of all those systems we may meet in the universe. What marks them?

They are found in or as *nature, life, humankind, mind, and society*. By the definition of their complex behavior, we consider these systems memory laden[12].

---

[12]Rheology, the study of the deformation and flow of matter, is also memory laden. It deals with simpler peculiar engineering materials such as paints, asphalts, rubber, sewage, silly putty, plastics and the like. Physically, these materials are even more difficult to understand than the homeokinetic systems, because

The Physics of Complex Systems

Complex systems arise from the forces that nature uses. We can do the physics of complex systems because we can recognize their conservations. And because nature is indefinitely repetitious. In complex systems, complex patterns repeat again and again. It is like a play that repeats with only moderate changes in its patterns. It is baseball played in myriads of ball parks for interminable innings.

---

almost all of the peculiarities lie in the almost non-generalizable details.

LESSON 5
PRINCIPLES AND APPLICATIONS[13]

We are in the pursuit of all the antinomies of understanding from a physical point of view of all the threads that are involved in the matter-energy universe around and within us. Antinomies are the paradoxes, not quite contradictory arguments and processes, that describe what is happening out there. Our pursuit of these is much like Aristotle's 'peripatetic' school. In attempting a static and dynamic resolution, we are concerned with stability of states and changes of state.

In these lessons, we want to get to two great antinomies:

- Is there a physical science for the biological system without vitalistic undertones?

---

[13]Revised from *A Course of Study on Homeokinetics: The Physics of Complex Systems: Principles and Applications, Bulletin 2, 1997*

- Is there a physical science for the human social system with explanatory and predictive power?

However, language is a very entangling web, loaded with meaning. It almost requires a thick book of unpacking for each word. That, in part, is the dilemma we face in an exposition of homeokinetics as a physics for complex systems. As a start, we lay out seven definitions and principles, and then describe a simple application of the principles in the modeling of a living system. With further extensions, this approach can be used to model social systems for modern humans.

Science

Science is a parsimonious, principled, systematic, and predictive description of things in nature.

System

A system is a bounded group of related formal, functional, or mentally constituted units that make up a unified whole (e.g., the world system; a philosophic system).

Physical Science

First among sciences, physics deals with the laws of movement and change in space and time in all material-energetic systems, under the action of forces. Not only are the systems bounded, but their units are atomistic. Thus, intrinsically, a micro and macro level of description exists in all physical systems, and it is necessary to relate them.

Key horizontal reductionism

The principles of physics stand off to one side; on a second side stands a nested hierarchy of the systems in nature. As currently understood, that hierarchy comprises:

- The universe
- Galaxies
- Intragalactic systems, including gas clouds, dust clouds, stars, planets, planetismals, also planetary subsystems including geochemical, biochemical, life, and society
- Atoms-ions-molecules
- Leptons-quarks
- A physical vacuum (an earlier age thought it to be turtles all the way down)

The two sides are connected by strategies. The corpus of physics consists of its pure principles and its hyphenated applications, e.g., cosmological physics, stellar physics, biophysics, social physics, nuclear physics, geophysics.

Modeling methodology

A force bounding enclosure is identified. Within that enclosure, a heterogeneous assemblage of atomistic units that can resist destruction are depicted. The system is developed through the character of the interactions under available forces of the atomistic units. Chemistry, for example, is the making, breaking, and exchanging of force-developed bonds among the units. There are only a very few basic forces. Systems emerge from the cooperation between attractive and repulsive forces. The atomistic units are in sustained motion. A physics of systems emerges basically from the capability to identify a limited number of process variables that are conserved by the interactive atomistic units during their interactions.

Modeling simple physical systems

In a simple ensemble system or collective with interactions by particle pairs under mechanical forces, the units exhibit conservations of:

- mass,
- momentum, and
- energy

With electrical forces, there is conservation also of:

- electric charge.

The continuing paired interactions quickly equipartition energy among all the atomistic players, resulting in a local regional equation of state at a macroscopic level (transforming microscopic measures of mass, momentum, and energy to macroscopic measures of mass density, pressure, and energy density or temperature which measures energy density per degree of freedom of movement. The equation of state is their interrelation). Besides equilibrium field processes described by an equation of state, there are near equilibrium steady flow and transient flow processes that can be described by equations of change. Such equations describe both:

- smooth or laminar flow fields, or
- turbulent and eddying flow fields

This description is good enough to deal with almost all flow processes in the universe such as the big bang expansion of the universe, motion in galaxies, in stars, in planetary plastic or fluid processes, such as magma, water, and atmosphere, blood flow, water and air transport systems, chemical flows. Extending solid state processes beyond their elastic limits also represents describable flow processes.

Modeling complex physical systems

In a complex ensemble or collective system, given that a persistent system emerges, there is a longer period of time rather than a few atomistic interactions, for which a near local equilibrium emerges. Our homeokinetic definition of a complex system *is a system which exhibits extremely long time delays in its complex atomistic interiors*. By this definition, a near equilibrium emerges in what we call the factory day of the atomistic units. There is nothing physically strange in the atomistic interactions. It is just that these interiors can be represented as internal fluid factories. The living organism, or the mass units in a complex atmosphere, exhibit such fluid complexity. A morsel of food enters the factory and it undergoes a great number of time-delaying internal transformations; or energy is tied up in a metastable water-bearing cloud. The conservations in such systems are somewhat transformed. Instead of only one mass conservation, there is a conservation of a number of mass species, allowing for chemistry via the electric force; there is the conservation of energy; but the conservation of momentum transforms into the conservation of action (the organized more macroscopic emergence of energy-time products from the complex unit factories — their 'actions'). The physical principle underlying the transformation is like Bohr's early quantum theory. In that theory, the mechanics of any fundamental particle interaction can be described by the following cycling form:

- The sum of momentum-displacement product interactions is measured by a small number of units of a fundamental 'natural' constant of action, Planck's constant h.

Our macroscopic form of that principle is that an energy-dissipating complex field unit expends a unit of factory day action which is characteristic of the complex atomistic species (note that according to the first law of thermodynamics, energy in the physical universe is neither created nor destroyed; but according to the second law it may be transformed dissipatively into lower, more degraded forms of energy). We have scaled that measure H for all mammals. It varies with the 0.80 power of adult body mass; illustratively, about 2,000 kcal-days of action per day for humans.

Modeling a living system

A complex living system adds what we may perceive to be one more conservation, the conservation of population number. Since living atomistic units are born and die, and by thermodynamic reasoning they cannot reproduce to infinite number nor do they very soon die out in normal reproducing time scales, we may assume that conservations of mass species and number separate (by directing the flow of material, we can raise many or few small or large plants or animals). Thus they represent independent components of the equations of state or change. We propose to show, in an indefinitely maintained flow field, that the equation of state of such a near steady flow field colony requires a relation among four conservations, flows for:

- mass species
- actions
- energy, and
- number

Note that a system was characterized as a bounded group of units organized into a field collective. That bounding may have been achieved by solid walls, elastic walls, an ingathering gravitational force, actually any force that would turn the movement inward by acting as a centering force.

Living Collection Example

We will apply these principles to a living collective—the simplest—a colony of flagellated bacteria. We will use the colony's own action spectrum to center its spatial location.

What is proposed is to maintain a single species colony of say 10,000 live bacteria in a particular region in a flow system. Take a U-tube and arrange a steady drip of water into that tube so that it overflows out in the exit end, say at a level a little lower than at the entrance end. By changing the difference in height, we can adjust to any velocity flow field that we wish to elect. Our proposal is to maintain a colony of bacteria in the entrance region of the tube at a definite number level. However, we propose to make them work at some reachable energy consumption level within their competence. That is why we have adjusted the velocity of the field. We propose to make them swim at that speed.

The external modes of action of flagellated bacteria are:

- incorporate chemical elements by diffusion,
- swim in a straight line by rotating flagella one preferred way, and
- tumble in motion by reversing that flagellar motion.

The empirical findings are that in favorable media, the straight line segments are longer. The resultant motion is an apparent diffusion up a favorable food gradient. In addition, there is a division period in which the bacteria divide in half (double their number) by reproductive fission. That time scale depends on temperature. A common temperature range is somewhere between near freezing and boiling water temperatures. A typical doubling time at room temperature may be in the vicinity of, say, 20 minutes. Thus one elects some in-between temperature to thermostat the flow system.

We have to know the energy consumption of our selected bacterial species when swimming in a stream of our elected velocity at our given temperature. We can perform tests on a small sample to determine that specific consumption, or we might make a crude estimate from our mammalian data. Such an estimate might come out in the vicinity of say 50 picograms (10^{-12} grams) per minute of glucose. So we add such a stream of glucose to our U-tube flow system.

What would happen if we put in one, a few, the number we wish to maintain, or many more of our desired bacteria? Obviously they would be swept along by the stream, but in the competition for the limited glucose supply:

(a) there would be continued growth and division, number doubling per 20 minutes, and

(b) by glucose depletion, there would form a gradient of glucose concentration in the stream, so that the more favorable region of occupancy is toward the entrance.

A diminishing exponential concentration would develop, concentrating the cell number up near the entrance. Is that the flow equilibrium resultant?

No, because the energy expenditure is for the dissipative cost of swimming. It does not supply the required material — proteins and nucleic acids — needed to maintain the bacterial body material growth supply. Thus, the doubling growth could not take place. Either the number growth would have to stop, or — if forced to continue — some cells would become moribund and die. Since they could not swim, they would be swept away.

Thus we see the additional conservation

condition. To maintain a dilute non-interacting colony of say 10,000 bacteria, we have to supply the material replacement for the bacteria that die and are swept away. We must add to our stream the required material flux in protein or amino acids and nucleic acids that are disappearing. If the various streams are correct in magnitude, then when we introduce whatever number of the pure strain we wish to maintain, it will move by fission and death toward the equilibrium in number, in action, in mass flow streams, and in the energy stream that represents one point in the equation of state for those bacteria at that operating temperature, with no unaccounted-for ingredients in the outflow. By repeating the experiment at different temperatures and velocities, etc., we can determine the entire mathematical relationship among the components of this four variable equation of state (This is as an idealized but realizable equation of state. There are some more dynamic unstable states for the bacterial processes which are possible, but we do not have to confront them in our first simple modeling). And then this can be done for other living species.

LESSON 6
PRIMER ON HOMEOKINETICS[14]

Defining Homeokinetics

The central task that homeokinetics takes on is the intellectual basis of explanation for essentially all the systems out there and inside ourselves. The term homeokinetics was coined *de novo* to represent complex systems of atomistic-like entities — *atomisms* — in which the time delay of action (the energy-time product of function) would represent a limiting long time scale, as a fundamental process, or a periodic reciprocal as a very low functional frequency, compared to the collisional exchange of action between or among neighboring atomisms. That is the operational definition of homeokinetic complex systems.

As a companion piece to that operational definition of homeokinetics, a logical-philosophic

---

[14]Revised from *Primer on Homeokinetics: A Physical Foundation for Complex Systems*, Cri-de-Coeur Press, Laguna Woods, CA, 1998. Presented at the 1998 Homeokinetics Conference, University of Connecticut, Storrs, Connecticut.

characterization for causality in complex systems is outlined in Iberall (1974). In that study[15], the operational chains of causality in a system are derived from a closed loop, e.g., a circular array of functional processes (achieved from the fumbling exploration of all available directions — this is exhibited both by persons and nature

This homeokinetic principle provides the foundation for a physical thermodynamics or a thermodynamics of engine processes. There is a path that connects A to B, in one or more steps, and B to A, but not in the same 'direction' (time frames). That is, thermodynamics represents a connection of two or more linked space-time processes (or a sequence in a higher ordered n-dimensional string of processes) which are both symmetrical in the time dimension, yet represent a pair that exhibits both symmetry and symmetry breaking (Why? Because the energy goes off in different directions and is lost to the particular system of isolated concern). A very simple illustration of that closed loop or circular chain of causality is the nonlinear coupling between the pendular motion and the escapement motion (its continuing search for escape from its detent) in a grandfather clock.

Physical causality is not a simple notion to understand particularly in complex systems, and it is key — in the end — for all processes. It is associated and arises — not only from the laws of symmetry in physics, but from the law of inhomogeneity in the universe of processes and how form-function emerge

---

[15]This first paper was inspired by Arnold Toynbee (1889-1975), Henry Margenau (1901-1997), and the organizing meeting of the ISCSC.

through dynamic change in the total universe of being.

Methodology for homeokineticists

How does homeokinetics operate to identify form and function, system and process—in classic Greek terms, the being now from the becoming before and after?

We suggest a methodology. First, choose your field and scale of observation. By definition, it puts you the observer into the picture, at your observation scale—of space-time, at a near negligible energy or action of interactions. Recognize this as a problem within the Bridgman view of instrumentalism whereby concepts of science are reduced or replaced by operations necessary to measure them. Evolving technology will improve measurements.

Secondly, learn all the possible directions you are 'free' to explore, the inhomogeneity of levels and columnar chains that seem to interact to produce form and function as in a system.

For the use of a language suited to homeokinetics, use the common language as found in a good dictionary. This follows the advice of the great mathematician Kleene who observes in his text on metamathematics that the logic he takes recourse to, for a start, is the common logic. He notes that if the student or scholar who wishes to pursue Kleene's subject is not willing to accept that starting point, then they should take up bee-keeping.

As you go up and down in a nested form, you will gradually learn about and appreciate that there is a 'vertical' hierarchy of interacting players. The hierarchy consists of a diversity of players who influence each other. That vertical array of influences carry the few — small number — of physical forces that create the beings, their states, and their becomings, their rates of motion and change.

Operationally, the observer will think through all four forces[16] to grasp what governs form and function. As a reminder, these are gravitational, electromagnetic, strong nuclear, and weak nuclear forces. Most commonly the electromagnetic and gravitation will be involved.

For homeokinetic purposes, we assume at any systems' level we examine, that these primitive or 'ur'-forces split their directions and entwine and mix so as to produce the higher-ordered forms of these forces applicable to the higher ordered, often complex, systems.

As a basic example of such higher ordering, consider the chemoelectric or electrochemical force forms that drive geochemistry, biochemistry, plasma physics, and the like. To a large degree, those higher ordered forces are derived from the electric force in vacuum interacting with the split path of the electric force in matter to produce the higher order of

---

[16]The four forces have been integrated into three, and may yet be reduced to two, and even one. In Newton's time, force was most commonly wrapped around a problem of "action at a distance," in which the nature of the gravitational force was a prime example. Currently, physical science regards them as "forces of exchange" in which an actual 'virtual' mass-energy particle (which is said to "carry the force") whizzes back and forth in space-time directions via a so-called vacuum to create the measurable strength of that force. That topic does not have to be elaborated on here in detail.

chemistry and its hyphenated forms. An interpersonal force between objects such as animals and people is even more complex.

Extending Physics to Homeokinetics

Starting from Newtonian mechanics in the late 17th Century, physical study was augmented to include: electricity and magnetism (later unified to electromagnetic theory), heat energy and thermodynamics, light and geometric optics (unified into electromagnetism); and chemical physics and atomic physics (which were then largely integrated in and with electromagnetism). In the 20th century, the new discovery of radioactive chemistry-physics resulted in a modified form of mechanics known as quantum theory (linking electromagnetic theory with a modified mechanics for matter-energy that was small and fast) and another form of mechanics known as special and general relativistic mechanics.

Physics as we know it now includes classical mechanics, quantum and relativistic mechanics, electromagnetism and quantum field theory, and thermodynamics.

But physics regards itself as being based on or as an experimental science. Its beauty — at least to physicists — is that in its long run, theory and experiment proceed historically apace. As a would-be branch of physics, we accept that fully in homeokinetics.

The problem that such a statement creates is whether every homeokineticist has to first or at some point master the discipline of physics. We have wrestled with that problem for perhaps 35 years, in almost every conceivable format. Our answer, still current, is not. We believe it is sufficient to be well-trained in any scientific discipline and willing to attend, and that physicists—through primers and examples—can impart a sufficient technical base to move it into a reasonable homeokinetic-based interdisciplinary science.

Physics deals with the forces and collective ensembles of organization, their laws and rules governing motion and change as well as steady states of little or no apparent organizational change. It deals with these collectives, most frequently isolatable systems, via a separation into hyphenated applied fields of study. Thus, cosmological physics on top, fundamental particle physics or physics of the vacuum on the bottom, and many intermediary fields in between, e.g., nuclear, atomic, geophysical, biophysical, even a social physics study.

Most of normal physics does not require our homeokinetic attention. The discipline is disciplined, it is largely reasonably trained, it has its mathematical and conceptual wizards, its literature is extensive and considerably self-corrective for its errors.

But physics has neglected complex systems with their very long internal factory day delays. These are systems associated with nested hierarchy and with an extensive range of time scale processes. The formal catch-phrase name on those complex problems is *nature, life, humankind, mind,* and *society.*

To paraphrase one of our colleagues, "all thoughtful scientists are reductionists," but the true problem remains the detailed path of a constructionist. As a generalist to whom that generalist path comes easy, my working colleagues and I can affirm endlessly the significance of the detailing, which we consider usually emerges from the engineering physics.

Homeokinetic Systems

At any complex systems level, what we find defining their complexity is likely a complex of formed subsystems whose association largely exhibits an extensive morphological collective — its space-like properties, and — particularly homeokinetic in character — an extensive spectrum of time-like properties as a spectroscopic collective. Our obvious inspiration for the latter came from the chemical atomic and nuclear spectra used for process identification in physics, or the extensive shake spectrum of processes used in engineering physics structures, e.g., testing a whole airplane, or the even more obvious one of the spectrum for hydrodynamic turbulence, or the dynamic spectrum of vital signs.

Another central characteristic of all complex system studies is that the field processes, those making up the total hydrodynamic-thermodynamic properties in the field in its spatial and temporal domains, were diffusive and wave-propagative local processes, and — more global in extension — convection.

Further, outstanding characteristics of those complex fields were their nonlinear characteristics stemming from the systems' thermodynamics, and minimally from the convection.

All fields, at their bottom, were found to be atomistic-like. Thus, the key homeokinetic problem is how the bottom collective structure and functions would be connected to the functionally remote character of the top collective.

It was possible to prove the following conjectures: That the diffusion process emerged as a collective process in the function of the collective processes above from random walk exchanges between and among pairs of atomistic-like interactions; that the wave propagative process emerged from coherent 'in-a-line' or other extended regular chains of interaction; while the convective global exchange emerged from the replacement of a small thermodynamic regional group, e.g., a cell of neighbors, replaced by a contiguous cell. Further it could be seen that these three types of organized movement or change were exhaustive for their 'directions' of occurrence.

Between the more normal physical constraints put on the lower atomistic level in any particular system, and the upper collective-like character of the top level in the system, lies all the intermediate structures and functions in that grand system level. That has to represent a third dynamic descriptive physics. We of course take our cue from a Navier-Stokes construct which is built up from the Boltzmann description. This of course asserts that we really cannot simplify that process more than to say one can either try to follow the mathematics-logic of that process, or take recourse to what we learned from Landau-Lifshitz. You can build up a view of a free energy function for a system from its observational characteristics. If you do that, you can acquire a reasonable sense of the system's intermediate dynamics equivalent to a Navier-Stokes description. While part of the standard statistical physics corpus, not too many people apply it in sufficient detail to grasp the difficulty and complexity it affords the investigator for complex systems. For homeokinetic systems, the problem is exacerbated by the extensive timing and phasing of the various periodic or quasi-periodic processes that are involved. This is further complexified if the range is sufficient to involve quantum states. The detailed problem is to be able to compute and couple the various components that make up real energy, and to determine if their phasing has any meaning, e.g., whether they are statistically independent. In a very important sense, perhaps even a little more complicated than Feynman diagrams, yet with some logical relation, homeokinetics whispers some such sum over states and phases problem, but of a more classical nature. Can we simplify this for a primer? That remains to be seen. So far we have always approached the problem by extensive experimental exploration of the repetitive quasi-periods in cycles, as a hallmark of homeokinetics and tried to see if we could follow the total system dynamics by individual relaxations in each conservation or so-called summational invariant.

The study of Feynman diagrams acquaints the student of field processes in quantum electrodynamics (QED) with this: the path that a field of photons, say, each individually located at its starting point, is determined by the path integral of the speed-of-light movement in all available media through all possible reaches through all of space. This at first seems so enormous a task, but as Feynman liked to point out, students learn the art in about two years. It consisted of learning quickly those path integral results that had null net occupancy, and to narrow down quickly on the few regions that would contribute changing motional paths. Thus QED became the *sine qua non* of results of extreme accuracy in physics.

In approaching more general kinds of fundamental particles, as quantum chromodynamics, not quite the same sort of precision is the result. Problems remain.

In homeokinetics, with complex associations involved in its atomisms, it is even more difficult for us to characterize the total path integral through all available space-time that a complex atomism will take. Would the reader feel comfortable in trying to characterize the path integral of a complex atomistic system like Tom Jones running through all the possible adventures he might have to meet head on in London, in England, and possibly Europe? Yet there is a possible statistics assignable to the task. It is very likely that the reviewer of Soodak and Iberall (1978) wanted us to tackle that sort of problem as a direction for us to follow then for homeokinetics. At that time we were not ready for the problem, and perhaps we just begin to appreciate its enormity in the complex systems case.

One of the first things we have had to realize is that we had to throw away dependence on continuum space-time variables. Thus, we have had to develop suitable computational canons to befit thermodynamically-constrained systems variables at top and bottom that are discrete. Differentiable function theory cannot be used. We can add up and approximate by simple continuous function over these systems with large numbers of atomisms. So our modeling, in some crude sense, can go down to collectives, e.g., little more than single cells with 7, 10, 20, 100 members. We really do not depend on law of large number averages for so-called mean state approximations.

Because of the extensive makeup of periodic properties and functional performance, we have had to concentrate on laws and rules for command-control of states. We regard that as a switching function that has to be regulated in its speed and direction of response. That problem operates by a system of chemical catalysts used dynamically as a language.

As a language in what we call a factory system because of operation in many modes of behavior, the language advances and retards the catalysis of messenger chemicals as regulatory chains. The language usage of the system controls its operation by catalysis of switch modes. It can operate in either a wired conductive mode or a 'to-whom-it-may-concern' flow conductive or convective mode. This is as far as we can go in a general description of the extension, transformation of normal physics to its homeokinetic expansion to complex systems.

Homeokinetics Doctrine

To observers such as us, the universe far outside of us seems to be so far removed that—by any of the signals we receive from out there—those signals seem hardly capable of being the received production of a homogeneous space-time expanse.

Thus we gradually infer an inhomogeneous universe out there with a considerable number of matter-energy clumpings. In fact, we tend to find and begin to expect form-functional strata arrayed in a variety of vertical and horizontal segments, also localized in point-like, sheet-like, and volume-like configurations.

Before the reader assumes that human complex configurations are the only such possible detectors, note that one finds configurational alignment among other animals, plants, planetary and stellar, and galactic, and small molecular arrays to the signals received from outside. The amount of detail of that mapping may be disputed, but, again, their true story is all in the details.

But that state of affairs is not only true for the grand universe outside of each individual atomism. It is also true for the interior of essentially every discrete or bounded complex system. One finds that in us, in other species, in planets, stars, and the like. These two conjectures, or noted observations, or rules, or laws are foundational in homeokinetics.

With that assertion, we believe we have established a base for the homeokinetic description that the matter-energy universe out there is a hierarchical system consisting of hierarchical organization as an alternation of levels of -A-C-A-C-, where A stands for an atomistic level and C denotes a collective level.

It is the homeokinetic conjecture that such an alternation takes place through all levels in our universe of observation until either a top or bottom level ends as either an A or a C level.

At the present, for example, our instrumental observational perceptions (organization of received sensations into perceptions and thence into cognitions, which represent unitarily grouped and named perceptions) find leptons and quarks at the bottom as an atomistic level, and at the top likely a cosmological atomism followed by a detailedly unknown vacuum collective.

Another detailed feature of that bounding vacuum collective level, is that its detailing cannot really be established only by the use of the four common 'directions', three space-like and one time-like. String theory calls for perhaps ten dimensions of inhomogeneity to understand the total space-time embedding.[17] But we are stuck with those systems closer to our more sharply perceived levels. And that is another homeokinetics doctrine.

We are complete reductionists of a physical persuasion but not simple vertical reductionists (e. g., that physics comes out of mathematics, chemistry comes out of physics, biology comes out of chemistry, psychology or ethology comes out of biology, and the like). Instead, off to one side, we have the principles of physics, and they connect — by strategies — to the systems in nature morphologically arrayed in nested forms.

We depict the problem in an engineering physics sense. We assert that you cannot run a factory in a compact space and time scale if every component at

---

[17]String theory is a substitute for a more compact, more 'spherical-like', more near homogeneous universe. Other physicists are evaluating these theories and they are not part of homeokinetics.

every level is constituted *de novo*. Instead you have suppliers at various levels producing and supplying components at varied levels, and it is that sort of upward and outward flow of materials, energies, and subunits of possible function which can run such a feasible homeokinetic universe of systems. If it doesn't fit, or the production price is too high, in suited time you get rid of it. That is our homeokinetics doctrine.

Our Nested Hierarchy

Once, some peoples believed that the systems all the way down were turtles[18], one on top of another. In a later version, the known world was placed in the middle surrounded by a glass-like remote revolving sphere holding all the star systems, except for a few wanderers.

A generally accepted popular view of our universe is as follows:

- a cosmological atomistic level;
- an atomistic galactic level with two major types of galaxies differentiated;
- an intra-galactic inhomogeneous collective of gas clouds, mainly hydrogen gas and perhaps one quarter helium gas, dust clouds containing atomic, molecular constituents manufactured in earlier generations of stars that have exploded in the past; a significant portion of the total matter in the universe in stars that are

---

[18]Before the science of astronomy, myths from China, India, and native Americans suggested that the world was supported by a World Turtle (or Cosmic Turtle). One answer to the question what holds that turtle up is an infinite regress of turtles.

continuing to be born, live, and die by what is essentially gas dynamic processes — these stars are largely arrayed in a so-called main sequence of stars of different sizes and types as they go through their history, whereupon they die either with a bang or energetically quiet whimper, possibly there is other matter or processes contained in this level which is said to be "dark" (not yet adequately detected) which may carry a larger segment of possibly missing matter or energy (just lately, evidence seems strong that highly abundant neutrinos actually with a small amount of newly detected mass, may make up some or all of that missing mass).

- planetary systems that formed as small nearly atomistic collectives among the stars which are produced mainly as binary pairs, secondarily as a star and trapped cold planets, and then lesser configurations;
- planetary atomisms as atomic molecular collectives of cold matter below perhaps 3,000-5,000K which will completely ionize (strip all surrounding so-called electrically negative electron clouds surrounding a positively charged central nucleus) all of its matter — these planets are attached by gravity force to their mother stars and also to 'sibling' smaller moons;
- 'burning' stars with an internal hot nuclear chemistry that represents a cauldron of production sequences producing a similar range of nuclear-atomic nuclei which make all

the elements with stability beyond hydrogen and helium, with greatest abundance up through the atomic weight of iron or nickel, and which results in the production of molecular materials that are connected as carbonaceous materials, silicic materials, and water related materials. It is that production sequence, properly located in temperature, these particular materials, and a silicic (silicon dioxide — sand) platform like on our sister planets, that is capable of producing life (this is our homeokinetic conjecture and we believe it to be a feasible experimental demonstration as an R and D project)(Robbins et al, 2015);

- the hot nuclear chemistry in stars and the cold atomic-molecular chemistry on planets are involved in the matter collective interactions all through the universe with a common list of feasible compounds, reckoned in the thousands or more among inorganic compounds, and in the millions for so-called organic compounds involving carbon and carbonaceous materials;

- the collective of positively charged nuclei number in the few hundred as stable or near stable isotopes of differing atomic mass and atomic number — they represent the stable configurations of collectives of fundamental particles;

- below that are the fundamental particles made up of or as leptons and quarks, in which the leptons are point-like particles like the electron and some nine others, and the quarks are primitive constituents of the so-called massy hadronic particles such as the proton, neutron and a number of other exotic particles.

• Among the atomic-molecular collectives that we may find on a planet are biochemical collectives that homeokinetics supposes arise and emerge from geochemistry, and thence life (Iberall, Wilkinson, and White, 1993);

• and a social physics emergent as a collective process among all—but to us notable—complex systems of life, particularly, mammalian, more particularly, primate, down to our human systems.

One does not have to memorize this list. But neither should one be surprised when some physical consequence of that lower story sticks out or forth into our daily lives. It may be a virus, a bug, a disease, a chemical corrective or poison, a manufacturing process, a failure of an institution that depends on some such detail. It may turn out that homeokinetics may have to augment other, more standard disciplines in order to understand such anomalies.

Principles of Complex Systems

In Iberall and Soodak (1987), we outline ten principles for a physics of complex systems. Assuming a zeroth principle, self-organization must start from modern physics itself, they follow:

Principle 1. All physical nature operates with only a few principles, but they acquire many forms and are expressed in a variety of emergent processes; the basic materials of physical systems throughout the universe are few; natural systems are acted on by only a few forces; the deep problem is to show how historical and evolutionary processes, with their diverse morphologies, arise from the operation of these fundamental elements.

Principle 2. Physical nature operates with only a few types of field processes: diffusion, wave propagation, convection.

Principle 3. A form emerges from interaction between two or more force systems. This process can be described as follows: matter and energy 'ingather' (an absorption process), are tied together coherently for an epoch, and then are released (an emission process). We refer to this asymmetric ingathering and release as a hop. The ingathering and release phases of form are unsymmetrical. In composite, the pair of processes represents a hopping Brownian motion, which we regard as a hierarchical version of Einstein's account of ordinary Brownian motion.

Principle 4. Emergence is a stability transition—new patterns or forms arise because changes of forces and scales make the existing patterns or forms unstable.

Principle 5. The basic physical laws of nature are expressed in terms of formal force systems scaled to the structures on which they act. The creation and stability of new forms require cooperation of two or more force systems, so that form and force systems entwine upon available material collectives and create new forms of greater size and time scale (e.g., molecules, cells, organisms, stars, galaxies, and societies). This is the principle of hierarchy.

Principle 6. Whereas the physics of simple systems deals with the organized space-time motion consequences (including rest states) of simple mean path-relaxation time movements of their atomisms, complex field systems manifest dynamic regulating behavior, describable in an action-space. Action is discretized into modes characteristic of the atomistic species. The physics of complex systems involves three largely independent phases in a grand dynamic pattern—a start-up phase in which complex systems assemble to make up the field system, a long life phase in which form and function of the field system are maintained by modal actions, and a degradation or dissolution phase.

Principle 7. A recurring ring of action modes in complex systems involves comparable (equipollent) energetics in each mode, with some small barriers between modes. Command-control systems must exist to relate internal and external events. That command-control is catalytic. The catalytic switchings that negotiate the barriers among action modes may be viewed as linguistic signals.

Principle 8. The distribution function characteristic of catalytic switch modes used as language is that of $1/f$ noise. Communication among complex autonomous units is just barely coherent.

Principle 9. The appropriate scaled physics at each level of organization is thermodynamic in nature.

Principle 10. Start-up in a system emerges as an S-shaped transition from stable near-homogeneous field I (the flatland of lower atomistic structure, which generally will contain homogeneous regions at its scale, such as gas or dust clouds in a galaxy out of which stars form) to stable near-homogeneous field II (the flatland of the higher level, e.g., a local community of stars).

Homeokinetic Applications

These final five sections will be very brief sketches of major problems under each major topic that homeokinetics feels competent to undertake. They are then also used to infer additional homeokinetic points to add to this primer.

A. Nature

In Iberall (1997a, p. 237), we referred to an experiment with a grandfather clock. This is a continuing but simplifying demonstration in homeokinetics of a low dimensional mechanical-thermodynamic 'dynamical system' which is not chaotic[19]. It consists of a simple compound two-second pendulum suspended on a hanger under a nonlinear pendulous escapement that draws a week's worth of gravitational energy from a chain carrying a mass which 'falls' in the Earth's gravitational field tick by tick as that tick-wise fall is released from side to side by detents.

---

[19]Some argue the noise in such a machine chaotic. See Abraham and Shaw (1992).

What we have done new for this primer is to interrupt our year and more long experiment. In that experiment, the clock with escapement has been gaining about 21 seconds per day at the current small nut-determining effective length of the pendulum for the past number of months in an autonomous time-keeping mode. We have then rewound the clock by raising the weight every seven days, discounting one day to permit the escapement to find each time its new phase, but using the cumulative time-keeping statistics of those independent six day epochs, which have averaged about 126 seconds gain per six days.

Our interruption has been to make a pendular length adjustment to some gain or loss per day closer to zero, and then to point out very simply what our tests and statistics have revealed. We can then ask the reader whether they are satisfied with our demonstration of no chaos and the generality of our demonstration.

Clearly, we will claim the following time scales and processes in our near-autonomous system. There is the two second (sec) pendular time scale with some nonlinearly determined spatial travel amplitude. There is a higher frequency small seismic signal of under Richter 3 magnitude — see Cal Tech reports every time they are called upon to show a shaking for the general region; loosely speaking, the energy is centered in the fractional sec time scale of frequencies; under higher seismic excitation, the pendular system exits from its simple near planar mode of swinging and goes through some wilder mechanical gyrations because of the very poor hanger suspension design, but it soon settles down back to the more nearly one degree of mechanical freedom motion.

The mechanical gearing to the 12 hour one revolution clock period creates a second or third major time scale. We use and report it as the composite of two such periods, effectively the solar day. The clock knows almost nothing about the day, so that its motion is nearly simple pendular, being compared with a more absolute time keeper of NBS/NIST time which is now stellar, planetary, solar, and atomic in its total scope.

We make two demonstrations of these theses. The pendulum and others like it have been tested hundreds and thousands of times at random and have shown their near isochronous pendular mechanical movement in a one dimensional response. For the sake of 'proof', we once again have tested our pendulum at amplitude levels from a standing start below the escapement coupling level to show its nominal isochronism, i.e. by counting swings per NBS/NIST time with a sufficiently accurate transfer clock. Secondly, we have shown that the pendular swings decay in angular amplitude in an exponential fashion proving linear thermodynamic loss. The major source of that 'damping' loss is the boundary lubrication in the support hanger. The proof of that is that the clock has to be oiled before some time, like a five-year period, otherwise the motion seizes and the clock stops. Other losses come from the gearing. Thus, at that point, the clock continues its period swing to period swing by the coupling with its escapement to produce either the daily cycle or a hidden cycle connected with the Q (quality) of the decay process. We determine the Q and that time scale by counting the number of swings before the clock comes to a halt or some fractional decay per near-isochronous time scale. By such counts, we find about 50 two-sec double amplitude swings — 100 sec worth of swinging with no escapement ticking. By observation of the small dial which enumerates the 60 ticks that make up the indicated escapement movement per 60-sec base cycle, we can observe the discrete escapement dynamics. Here it is very clear that the escapement is poorly designed. Instead of getting clean 60 ticks per minute, that dial indicated slips, stops, stutters, even if the entire cycle in invariably repeated. What is clear that after rewinding the clock — namely, changing the phase relation of the escapement to the swing pendulum — there is another time scale representing the time it takes for the escapement to find its commensurate or coherent weakly coupled process to the swinging pendulum's phase. (At present, we believe that upon rewinding the escapement chain, the escapement delays its impulsing by about 13 seconds in the next few minutes, with essentially no interference with the pendulum beat, so that indicated time of the small escapement dial falls behind that amount of indicated time for the next seven days until the clock is rewound. It has taken us a long observation time to grasp that the loss was not spread over the entire seventh day of winding or even a few hours, but effectively all in a few minute revolutions of the escapement cycle and its drive for the geared clock hands. We have no desire, at present to account for or to redesign the escapement).

Out of this complex of time scales, including an unregulated outside temperature, even a very small barometric pressure scale of variation, we can report the following. With the transfer means we use – in a time window early in the morning, half stumbling in the dark – it is difficult to note time coincidence for periods shorter than one sec, or at best with a glimpse of a half sec resolution. Thus our fastest time scale of observation, the number of seconds change from day to day has a statistical error of about a sec or two. We record our data as the number or seconds change from day to day. Thus a time sequence like 20, 24, 22, 27, etc. As we have said, the precision error of those reports may be a sec or two. The statistics of those data have a distribution that is nearly a standard, or usual, truncated Gaussian error form with a standard deviation of about 1.8 sec. In particular, we use the cumulative form of the distribution to estimate the mean time scale and its deviational characteristics. Thus, the linear isochronous clock trend and variance would be reported as about 21.8 sec +/-1.8 sec.

That is the statistics for the individual daily cycle. It agrees with the measurement precision and really has no surprises in it. But then we are also able to demonstrate the six day average, which we have imposed because we have to wind the clock to restore the energy, and because of a poor and limiting escapement design, we have to interrupt for a seventh day not to introduce a very peculiar phasing error from the escapement (we call it a daily slitching error for that one seventh day). That is not what a simple correct escapement should do. We could handle it by a second similar clock wound out of phase by 3-4 days from this clock to carry us over the day of winding change, but the story is transparent.

Our six day statistics is similarly truncated Gaussian, and centers around 126 sec loss with a variance of about 126 +/-1.8 sec. Thus, we find the second result of about 21.8 sec daily gain and a variance of about +/-0.3 sec and that is very striking. It is indicative of no mathematical chaos for this low dimension nonlinear mechanical-thermodynamic system, simply a Gaussian or Maxwell-Boltzmann statistical physics distribution function.

With our new pendular setting, all our preliminary tests lead us to believe that we will achieve the same precision in our variance. Having taken a day to adjust and estimate the trend we have succeeded in setting it to less than one second gain or loss per day. Now we have to take weeks to find out what our trend and variance really is over the 6 day week data statistics. We have little doubt (now none) that it will be very different from +/-0.2-0.3 sec per day. Our results are comparable with the NBS/NIST derived value for g, the Earth's gravity, of 980.665 cm^2/sec with a variation of about 1-2 units in the last significant figure which was done in the laboratory by an earlier occupant from whom the lab was inherited. This part in a million variance was achieved from a much more thoughtfully designed pendulum and escapement.

Are there new homeokinetics principles? Not really, except to stress how important it is in a Bridgman sense to have a rather full idea of all the essential time scales that you need understand in a complex system; that mathematics is not the same as the physics, that lots of things exist and remain in the engineering physics; that you most often will have to pursue both a continuum-like and a discrete-like mathematical description; that you will always be safer if you integrate and compare, rather than attempting to differentiate; to watch out all the time for hidden variables, and — as the most stringent part — while you may continue to build on the back of others, you very often will have to depend only on your own first principles' study to find out who is telling the truth; also be very willing to find yourself wrong.

B. Life and its Speciation

Rather than being a specific homeokinetic point devoted to life and speciation directly, this point will offer a description of a very simple element which can serve quite generally to urge [to force or impel movement in an indicated direction] a thermodynamic engine from mechanical parts and which is quite possibly an early forerunner for the evolution and development of a great number of Nature's self-organization of forms and functions, even complex ones. The unit considered is the bang-bang or oil can oscillator — a homeokinetic oscillator of some generality.

The human mind, as does nature (both complex systems), operates by a peculiar fumbling mode which we have identified and named in homeokinetics as *reverie* (lost in thought in that CNS known as the human mind). It suggests that each such ex- or incursion has its typical space and time action of coursing.

Here we wish to put forth an energy storing nonlinear element that, if it finds itself coupled by accident (or 'design'), furnishes the basis for a common oscillatory system. The element is a bistable elastic element, one that was used by Euler to illustrate the instability of the buckling column or strip under axial load, and by Poincaré in the snap action plate under edge compressing load in the plane of the plate. Simple illustrations of immediate demonstrability are a thin rod or strip, cover of a packet of matches, or the like. Involving further preparation is an oil can bottom. The snap motion is found illustrated by rods, strips, plates, shells, etc., put into such fixed compression at near a critical point of strain-energy stored mechanically in an elastic volume. The energy to snap the element in a direction of use from 'stable' position I to 'stable' position II can be made very small.

To complete a simple form of a mechanical oscillator capable of delivering power (such as a jack hammer), we will illustrate one that we tested and developed into a power tool. We took an oil can, affixed a power delivery rod external to the snap diaphragm, cut off much of the spout and threaded into the remaining internalized spout section a valve-containing block consisting of a discharge orifice, an internalized and guided ball valve attached to a long rod that could reach internally to the snap plate when the ball and rod were pushed through the orifice and seated on its beveled lip, and a conical spring mounted on the external face of the block to put inward bearing sealing force on the ball valve against its seat. If the diaphragm was not in contact with the rod, the ball was pulled down into its valving seat closing off the oil can chamber. If the oil can bottom was snapped down, it would deflect the rod and ball assembly into an open position, opening the oil can chamber to leakage in of air into the can volume. A vacuum pump source was affixed to the side wall of the oil can to create suction in the can to cause the can bottom to snap inward.

The flow rate of the vacuum source and the oil can chamber would determine the rate of restoring a critical suction at which the oil can bottom would snap and open the rapid inward leaking of air into the oil chamber. At that point the outward mounted power rod could deliver a hammering power impulse, like a jack hammer to an outside load, e.g., we first demonstrated that it could hammer in thumb tacks.

We then developed the principle into an air tool like a jack hammer. This is a thermodynamic oscillator or DC to AC converter, taking energy from an air supply and converting, by a nonlinear escapement-like device, into a mechanical energy elastic energy power impulsing stroke. It is not meant to be spectacular, just insidiously general, homeokinetic, e.g., as an additional hand-held power tool for shaping metal. Part of our definition of a complex system, in explaining the meaning of its language, is that it represents a tool used to augment the flow of action. A tool was defined as a material-energetic entity, neither self nor outer world, which could be interposed between self and outer world to augment action.

To extend this idea into life and its speciation, you can generalize it into many other forms. Consider any other continuing flow source of energy, e.g., a human who eats regularly—metabolizing chemical food energy for energy and then stores the available source energy in various storage bins—muscles, liver, and the like. Consider that he or she is a nonlinear marginally-stable storage source who can self-urge those sources he/she carries into an almost nondenumerable number of directions (e.g., he/she does not even know how to count them all unless confronted by many signaling scenarios). The body can then snap into a direction. It does that in stock market decisions, by elites or ordinary folk who have to make important or trivial decisions all the passing time, by people who are always taking one or the other or binary decision mind sets, e.g., to trade or to rob, to persuade or to take, to buy or to sell, to be or not to be, to kill or not to kill, to eat or not to eat, to scratch or not to scratch a body itch.

Further, you can get simpler and go at it at the very beginning of the life process, or at the time of any transition, e.g., even as speciation development or evolution. Think about the very primitive chemical links and chains by which nonlinear chemical steps or processes emerge from any streams of energy flow. It becomes 'mere' homeokinetic exercises to work out feasible urge paths. This is a primer, so think further. If any one such step is entrained and encoded, an organism can diversify and use that one step as a base for further development of interacting or synergetic engine processes and let complexity truly develop by homeokinetics. That's the foreshadow and the forecast.

Let us share an even more striking illustration of the generality of what we are discussing here.

Consider first a current bit of standard physics, the demonstration that neutrinos have likely been shown to possess or exhibit mass as well as energy. If true, the large number of flux of neutrinos may account for some, if not all, the missing mass in the universe that most physicists would like to find in place to make the cosmological modeling task simpler.

The problem has occupied physicists since the conceptualization of the neutrino. Those studies do not need homeokinetics.

However, the analogous problem in complex systems, such as living, on to human, is somehow trickier. That problem similarly can be stated by the depiction of two mass-energy atomistic-like particles passing each other with very weakly interacting forces whose complex character we do not quite understand yet (they are not new forces, but complex entanglement of the known forces, and capable of becoming saturated or shielded by having to engage in too many force bondings). The question that concerns us, in a homeokinetics sense, is to what extent might there be some mutual entrainment, some more permanent mark left after the passage. That is a key homeokinetic problem in a dynamic impulsive sense.

We have enough reason to believe that the effect of such encounters may be zero; minimal and trivial; momentary; lasting, but fading; lost in memory banks, but lasting tucked away as one more long term memory stored out there, without cluttering up the memory banks.

Happenings can occur in what we view as the 6 sec stream of cognition, going on as 15,000 signaling bits per day, in which the interperson interactions involving that persistent scaling provide very little bonding unless they are spectacular or persistently repeated — with almost only noisy passing interaction. Illustrations can be seen as follows. The first happened in 1998. Four years after Orange County, California, had been driven into bankruptcy, a judge orchestrated a $400 million settlement from Merrill Lynch. Two years of orchestrations by one judge managed to keep the lawyers (weak but persistent county attorneys and Merrill Lynch's super attorney who was hired expressedly to avoid any such settlement) bent into the shape, one lawyer against one lawyer. The passage of the two lead lawyers had no direction of such lingering action influence attached to their compulsive meetings.

The second relates to the re-intersection of two Christian faiths that separated permanently 450 years ago — the Protestant break over doctrine led by Luther from Mother Catholic Church. The issue was whether one accepts only belief in Jesus Christ as the condition to go to heaven or whether good works while living are required. After decades of dialogue, the Lutheran World Federation and the Roman Catholic Church arrived at an accord in 1999, the "Joint Declaration on the Doctrine of Justification." Twenty years of persistent hammering by representatives from both organizations (complex systems) have been devoted to find a path, a direction of common agreement.

You may regard it as peculiarly a human intellectual exercise; we regard it as homeokinetics, a higher ordered chemistry of the CNS, or a command-control system in any complex system. More compact space-time interactions, intersections take place in elections. We mention them later on.

C. Humankind

Humankind constitutes one species of living organisms. It forms a collective known as Homo sapiens sapiens. Phylogenetically, it is a collective nested among a higher collective, the genus Homo, who are nested among the family of hominids, beyond are hominoids, then anthropods nested among the order primates, up into the class of mammals, then as vertebrates who are nested among primates, who are nested among the phylum of chordates, who then belong to the animal kingdom (which is one of five kingdoms). The evolutionary, developmental, diversification of this fantastic complex of chemically emergent forms is a great challenge.

In Iberall, Wilkinson, and White (1993) and our other work on the biochemical foundations model built on a geochemistry model, we explore the evolutionary problem. In one sentence, the question is how to resolve the problem of evolution in the difference between a so-called punctuate form of widely separated time scales and a more nearly near-continuous record of producing and creating diversified species.

For background, two different descriptive sources might be of assistance. Young (1971) is written from the point of view of a neurobiologist with wide learning. De Laet *et al* (1994) is written from the point of view of two handfuls of world-dispersed paleobiologists and paleoanthropologists organized as a second group effort under UNESCO sponsorship. Using the mammalian class, we note a somewhat common body plan and brain command-control organization (see, for example, Havez, 1962 or Gerstner, 1992). More to the point for homeokinetic inferences, the class members' phoneme language of dynamic fragments and their organ chemical functions and catalytic languages are generally quite similar. Secondly, this is even more specialized and common at the primate level (see, for example, the ethologist John F. Eisenberg's two articles on their common behavior). Above that there is even greater commonality at the hominoid and hominid level even if the latter is more inferential. Here we recommend de Laet *et al* (1994).

So we effectively have to look at an almost last branching at perhaps 300,000 ybp (years before present). In principle, we can essentially imagine a relatively common branching in form and function as of that scale from very close relatives of the Homo erectus nurturing species and an almost irrelevant branching off of Homo sapiens neanderthalensis. There are some more modern details which can interpose one or more subgroups at that junction but they count for little, except a modest number of point mutations. So what do we find at that sort of junction for the range of dynamic behaviors?

We find the small group band structure that will persist almost unchanged over the next 300,000 minus 10,000 years. Humans by then were superb hunters (the now known record of spears with hardened points) and gatherers. We already know of a 3,000,000 year history of evolution of stone tools at what can be estimated is a rather uniform rate. Thus, that Homo brain structure and function was already on a modern track rate. If one tracks an incrementally changing level of tool development, at what we call an adaptive steady rate to the emergent exigencies, one can see it keeping track in its dispersing rate with changes in the chemical-physical environment.

George P. Murdock's *Ethnographic Atlas* (1957) offers statistically standard behavioral patterns in all primitive cultures of band societies under a few hundred in localized population (clustering densities of less than 0.1 to 1 person per sq mi). To help understand this, one can look at such books as Chapple and Coon (1941), Service (1958), Service (1963), Harris (1968), Polanyi, Arensberg & Pearson (1957), or Moore (1992) (the latter having a homeokinetics bent).

This small group band lifestyle brings us up to about 40,000 ybp, without any significant break. At 40,000 ybp, there is a cultural stability transition. Thence, from 40,000 to 10,000 ybp, there is steady population growth at a constant rate and density (more area of the Earth's surface becomes included in the pattern. One can say that the low social vapor pressure is climbing somewhat as the rural density stays nearly constant but the small clustering concentrations increase the more global density).

During this time period, the technological rate potential makes a transition to a higher order of catalytic language complexity. Abstractions as represented in art and utilitarian functional forms begin to emerge. Those emergences, in a common language are 'stands for' or complex representational forms. These are the Venus figures and other denoters of a more abstract language. In a homeokinetics sense, we conjecture that another intermediate layer of neurons have evolved which have the extra capability to be used as denoters, an added language level to the many that already exist. One might say that the person now 'knows that he/she knows.'

Why is that language possible or appropriate? Because, as Darwin began to explore, one can test psychologically what types of information primates of various levels can recognize—things, markings, signals associated with their bodies—in mirrors or other self-referrals, and one can see the level of growth or change in that depiction. This literally is 'monkeying' around with what is inside that can recognize both material outside and inside, and it is a form of Feynman signaling that we refer to elsewhere. There is a change as of 40,000 years ago and in the representative nature of the new artifacts associated in number and viewed as complexity in cultural artifacts from that time on.

In Iberall, Wilkinson, and White (1993) and other work, we trace the development of cultural artifacts and technological gain in amplification of action from that time. It is no surprise that the cultural developments segue into the use of vegetable, animal, and mineral resources, and their amplification by more overt languages for control of group behavior.

By this sort of schema, we manage to trace and predict and account for cultural, demographic, material, energetic, action streams by which humankind develops, first before 40,000 ybp, then up to 10,000 ybp, and then into rather recent times. We take note of the break at the so-called demographic transition and bring our story both predictively and retrodictively up to the present.

D. Mind and Brain

In our grandfather clock homeokinetic argument for nature, we had only to consider the interaction back and forth of a pendular system and an escapement system in an external gravitational field. Here now, we wish to examine the scattering and propagation[20] by means of interactions of the person with inner and outer escapements, entrainments like our hopping Brownian motion, bonding and force repulsion, also with external fields.

In many of my papers, I have started to build a base for a person-level homeokinetics spectrum in mind and body, both as processes and forms that deal with the instrumental view of those chemical-physical functions and forms. For example, I have identified a considerable number of time scales. See Iberall & McCulloch (1969), Llinas & Iberall (1977), Iberall (1992, 1995, 1997a, 1997b), Iberall & Wilkinson (1997), Iberall, Wilkinson, White (1993).

That modeling goes from the senses and

---

[20]This refers to the Feynman program in quantum electrodynamics (QED). For the forewarned, the simplest glimpse for gleanings of this way be found, say, in Lerner and Trigg (1991, pp. 380, 969, 974). As the first article author starts out, "Feynman diagrams...are graphical representations of...theory involving the scattering and propagation of interacting particles". In QED, only electrons, positrons, and photons are involved without external fields, but we have to integrate our answers over an entire universe of 4 dimensional space-time fields.

sensations in the body (basically of all mammals) at the sensory organ receptors out to a few tenths to 1 or 2 seconds, then to the integrative perceptions which unite a sheaf of sensations into a unity at the few seconds level. At that level in the hierarchy of awareness, cognition is formed as a command-control selection or choice of which of the signaling perceptions throughout the entire body gets the attention. That is quite well up in higher reaches of the brain. Operating in the 1 to 10 sec range as a persistent stream of about 6 sec average mean time signaling complexes, it represents an almost continuous flow of about 15,000 streaming signals that are constantly forming and telling the organism's ongoing story. That level (see Gerstner, 1992) constitutes the phonemic level of signaling in effectively all mammalian CNS systems.

In our conjecture, the fuller content of languages begins at the level of various kinds of chemical processes, both wired in the nervous system and conductive to-whom-it-may-concern signals, e.g., neuroendocrine, in the blood. Past the faster endocrine flows, one finally gets to the slower time scales, some species' dependent, others not, until one gets to about a three-hour time scale which seems to be chemical thermodynamic closure in the person's organism. Beyond the three-hour scale, one gets to time scales and processes that are more related to social physics and chemistry.

Given that there is a continuing extensive spectrum out to the life span, such as near 100 years for the person in human demography, and beyond out to 500 years for civilization, and then beyond to speciation throughout a 3.8 billion year (Gy) epoch, what do we learn about the intermediate time scales that represent the scaling and effect of command-control as we ordinary observers of ourselves might cogitate?

Unfortunately, our characterizations of the homeokinetic nature of that scaling is still vague (as seen in Iberall, Wilkinson and White, 1993, Chapters 4 and 6, particularly pp. 146-148). A static view of the true neurochemistry, as chemical languages, in the mammalian brain is seen in Jacobowitz (1998). The study is not easy. The gap between the atomistic level in the nervous system, e.g., as one might find it in Higoshida *et al* (1993), or the classics like E. Crosby or Arnold B. Scheibel's work, is enormous.

We offer a caricature for such a process of formation of an evolving human 'personic' group scenario of some significant sheaf of autonomously organizing dynamic trajectories. It may begin from starting impulses of a political person, or clique, or clan, or spin doctor, or advertising executive, or political move to start a war, or change a belief system, or to create a lynch mob, or the like. Thus a new idea or thought is thrown out, e.g., it is picked up in a public medium such as a newspaper or leaked into a reporter's ear.

Within the time scale of two days, opinions begin to form about it. An elite leadership, who wants to take some control of the movement, generally has to react in a few days. By about three days, there begins to be a social division for or against the idea. Regardless of how or why they may accept or reject the idea, there begins to arise a feasible conductive constituency for and against the idea, in percentages of about 20-40 percent for, and similarly 20-40 percent against.

Anyone who explores the rationality of this so-called sapient species alignment is in for surprise or disappointment. There is nothing rational about it. It literally is an emergent neurochemistry related to chemical behavioral formation that developed in childhood in perhaps the first month or two of infant nerve formation.

We have tried to trace it through a Freudian lens (e.g., 1949, 1954, Outline and Origins of Psychoanalysis; Projects for a Scientific Psychology) and its various derivative followers. We have explored the library of his teacher — Jean-Marie Charcot — at Salpetriere for turn-of-century writings which led to an engineering and scientific theory of communications and command-control, in all ancillary fields.

Even though a theory of information flow has emerged, its connection with the neurosciences has not been there. We are partisan enough to believe that Jacobowitz' effort can finally get us there in its pursuit of the chemical architectonic languages of the brain.

Continuing the scenario, the remainder of the society that cannot make up its mind and take a stand, perhaps 20 percent, sometimes more, furnish the swing vote that the leaders of the organizing group and/or the elite leadership in society, or the opposition, have to try to win over. Again, there is nothing rational in their effort. They find and explore all propaganda or emotional or monetary or reward means that they can to influence the swing group.

Picture the incessant stream of 6 sec phonemes, 15,000 a day crossing individuals' minds. In about 30-60 days of such signaling, some bias begins to be put into the organization of mind paths. But as directors of polling organizations state, there is no settling down of outlook until about 6 weeks before an election or choice has to be made.

Do you accept this depiction for the intermediate time scales, as an orchestration of the various clocking processes that go on in brain structure and its mind function through only neurochemical processes?

What we are observing is how divorced from any real attachment the human person has to the true value of his/her ideas. There appears to be a great deal of passion, but it is empty, devoid of human attachment. We have derived this by noting the difference between attachment to conservative or liberal ideas of operation and the extreme wing attachments to what are effectively religions and cults. But we cannot take a stand yet in our physical belief system on what this means for homeokinetics theory.

As a measure of empty punditry that we have observed by our national managerial elite for the past generation, we see two responses. If things are going well, we hear, "Don't bother us with such a pessimistic picture; the sky is the limit." On the other hand, if times are bad, their reply is, "Who cares about what may happen, the bottom is falling out of things." This pair of responses we characterize by the assertion that the common judgments are orthogonal, or very nearly, so to the course of historical truth. And in that sense, we find it very difficult to work for most managements.

What have we learned as new homeokinetic principle points? Clearly our concept of parallel small energy catalytic languages and power chemical processes at every complex system layer has to be true to provide any organizational stability. Our existing stable systems have to be many layered and subject to multi-hierarchical control. And that control has to be free of affective organized content.

We operate with a broad panoply of feasible chemical directed emotions, and they just ripple over us from childhood formations. It is not the libido of sex, or power, or the like. It is some sort of coherent language structure that we each use. It differs from everyone else's, and/but the others think they understand it but they don't.

It works good enough for governing purposes. I have detested that sentence since I first went to work for government in 1940. It is with a great shock that I finally stumble on its intrinsic truth in the general case of complex system command-control.

E. Society, Particularly Human

The saga of trade and war in human social history is civilizational with technological augmentation. The homeokinetics comments here are formed from work done with Frank Hassler, a nuclear physicist with the Department of Transportation, and with the homeokinetic development and evolution of a social physics work done through The International Society for the Comparative Study of Civilizations (ISCSC). Hassler and I have been developing a quantitative model of civilizations and their operational dynamics.

153

Humans have been integrated into civilizations and their precursors for the past 18,000 years. The emergent form is a locally dense population of persons organized into urbanized settlements within a sparser, more uniform, rural population. The centers of concentration are bound into collectives of perhaps a few hundred miles in compact area, and the broader collective of such politically bound units interacts weakly or loosely into what is referred to as an ecumene of such political units. Politics refers to the highest local order of command-control by some sprinkling of elite or high energetic leaders.

This array is complex because of the very extensive memory function that is involved in its persistence. The main processes that govern it are trade and war. Why? Because the total flow of materials and energy cannot be provided only by pair by pair interactions or small group interactions as had occurred earlier in hunter-gatherer societies. But the match in such flows and their mismatch at a time scale of the human generation tended to guarantee the dissonance of war (see, for example, Iberall 1973).

In the distant past, the hunter-gatherer small band configuration came apart and reformed anew every few years. In civilization, the match of the collective configuration with the greater stability furnished by more nearly solid state institutions, a social memory, and a persistent technological flow as a rate potential, resulted in achieving a stability more like 25 generations, i.e., 500 years.

With no room for doubt, as physicist collaborators, we recognized the process as a vapor phase collective operating under low vapor pressure (the low density rural population) with condensed liquid droplets (the collective urbanized centers). These latter in time would evaporate and reform. At the same time, within the condensed droplets, there would be institutions of more nearly solid plastic form, some as organs, others as other chemical impurities or material forms partly restrained in motion by stronger than liquid bonds.

To avoid this appearing metaphorical, consider the architectonics of a house. Here we ask recall of Jacobowitz (1998). A house looks like a solid structure, commonly in some early mythic period of its ownership. As time goes on, repair and replacement represent a near continuum-like flow of materials, costs, and action streams to keep it working. To the maintenance engineer, it is a steady flow process from the very first day of operation. The process is architectonic, not simple architecture, not a one shot construction. That is a very homeokinetic principle.

Through our work with political and other social scientists, we have uncovered quite a few homeokinetics principles of some additional interest.

For example, as large structure social time scales, we have identified the time scale of 4 hours as the top scale of biophysical organization of the individual person, the scale for chemical thermodynamic near equilibrium. Thus work organization, restaurants, and the like, illustrate social attention to that scale. Then there is the Earth day, whose daily night-day forming process accounts for the social regulation, e.g. by mayors, of that scale.

Beyond that is the 30-60-90 day scale related to

seasons and mood and mode changing. A society based on agriculture and animal husbandry finds it necessary to attend to that scale through all its operating activities.

The next integrative time scale is the solar system year, which binds the seasons and all the trophic webs on the Earth together. Corporate entities tend to do their system accounting at that scale.

Beyond is a 3-6 year scale that tends to represent scaling for the political command-control, with some added complexity for the economic scaling of the very general trading process and/or war process. The war process is governed by a focused question: Is it cheaper to trade or to rob and pillage?

We can then pass through the life death process of demography which deals both with a generational scaling — passing of the guards task, on through the one or two or three generation life scale. And so we finally arrive at the 500 year or so life of civilizations scale.

In and among that very extensive quite dense homeokinetics social spectral scale, we also find those process lines that accentuate the trade and war saga. Thus, introduced to the theme by the Foundation for the Study of Cycles (based on the research of Edward R. Dewey (1895-1978)), I have pursued and sharpened up data and causality for a generational scaling in near periodic process of war concentrations in the general ecumene for the past 2-3 millennia. On the other hand, Wilkinson, following the lead of the Cambridge hydrodynamicist Lewis Fry Richardson (1881-1953) in his *Statistics of Deadly Quarrels* (1950), has sharpened up the study of an approximate 4 or so year period in smaller wars within ecumenic groupings. By working with social scientists (e.g., ISCSC Society for the Study of Peace), we could offer a physically-based scientific account and then begin to carry it further to help them to a reasonable based science for their general fields. Thus. in our view, a physical base for trade and war is an essential ingredient for understanding a human social physics.

Beyond that, we begin to contend that this concept is more general for all complex system collectives and their societal or collective dynamics. There always exists the possibility of some form of strong and then weak binding, through a process of saturation between pairs of atomisms. That then raises a stability question. Should a next binding take place to the one unit, or to the few units, or to the many units? That sort of question really originated with Aristotle as a political question, and it still remains a physically-based political question. Who rules? This is the question for a theory of the elite command-control.

In Iberall (2000), I discuss command-control among humans. However, more broadly, the paper refers to command-control among all complex systems. By this time, we have looked at the problem from the point-of-view of all of the following incomplete list of academically-recognized disciplines: psychologist, psychiatrist, ethologist, ecologist, biologist, physiologist, pharmacologist, neurologist, neurochemist, biochemist, physical chemist, anthropologist, sociologist, politician, economist, lawyer, priesthood, religionist, philosopher, logician, physicist.

We have used the general concept of a 'value' system as *a* or *the* potential driving command-control. Our homeokinetic analysis is still far from complete or yet adequately determined. Our fundamental hope is that its complete ultimate reduction may take place in and by a hardnosed science combining pharmacological and physiological neurochemistry, and biophysics-biochemistry of a system's homeokinetic kind, but this may be a false hope.

References

Chapple and Coon, *Principles of Anthropology*, Polk, 1941.

de Laet et al (eds). *The History of Humankind*, NY, UNESCO, 1994.

Gerstner, G. Quantifiable Temporal and Spatial Behavior Patterns in Six Mammalian Species, Parts I and II, PhD Thesis, *UCLA Department of Neuroscience*, 1992.

Harris, M. *Rise of Anthropological Theory*, NY: Crowell, 1968

Havez, E. *The Behavior of Domestic Animals*, Baltimore: Williams and Wilkins, 1962.

Higoshida *et al* (eds), Molecular Basis of Ion Channels and Receptors Involved in Nerve Excitation, Synaptic Transmission and Muscle Contraction, *NY Academy Science Annals*, 1993.

Iberall, A. S. *Toward A General Science of Viable Systems*, NY: McGraw-Hill, 1972.

Iberall, A. S. On the Neurophysiological Basis for War, *General Systems Yearbook*, XVIII:161, 1973.

Iberall, A.S. On A Thermodynamic Theory of History, *General Systems Yearbook*, XIX:201, 1974.

Iberall, A.S. Does intention have a characteristic fast time scale? *Ecological Psychology*, 4, 39-61, 1992.

Iberall, A.S. A physical (homeokinetic) foundation for the Gibsonian theory of perception and action, *Ecological Psychology*, 7(1): 37-68, 1995.

Iberall, A.S. Nonlinear Dynamics From a Physical Point of View, *Ecological Psychology*, 9(3): 223-244, 1997a.

Iberall, A. S. A Friendly Countercomment to Holton, *Comparative Civilizations Review* 35: 63-66, Winter 1997b.

Iberall, A.S., What Makes Sammy-Samantha Run and Other Mammals Run? A first round of closure: *Ecological Psychology.*, 12:109-139, 2000.

Iberall, A.S. and McCulloch, W. S. The organizing principle of complex living systems. *Journal of Basic Engineering.*, ASME, 290-294, 1969.

Iberall, A.S. and Soodak, H. A Physics for Complex Systems. In F. E. Yates (ed) *Self-Organizing Systems, The Emergence of Order*, NY: Plenum Press, p. 499-520, 1987.

Iberall, A. S. and Wilkinson, D. On Understanding Language, *Comparative Civilizations Review* 35: 67-86, Winter 1997.

Iberall, A.S., Wilkinson, D., and White, D. *Foundations for Social and Biological Evolution*, Laguna Hills, CA: Cri de Coeur Press, 1993.

Jacobowitz, D. *Chemoarchitectonics of the Developing Mouse Brain*, CRC Press, 1998.

Lerner and Trigg (eds) *Encyclopedia of Physics*, 1991, pp. 380, 969, 974.

Llinas, R. and Iberall, A.S. A global model of neuronal command-control systems, *Biosystems* 8:233, 1977.

Moore, A. *Cultural Anthropology: The Field Study of Human Beings*. San Diego, CA: Collegiate Press, 1992.

Murdock, G. *Ethnographic Atlas*, 1957.

Polanyi, K., Arensberg, C., and Pearson, H. *Trade and Market in the Early Empires*, NY: Free Press, 1957.

Robbins, E.I., Kourtidou-Papadeli, C., Iberall, A.S., Nord, G.L., Jr., and Sato, M., From Precambrian Iron-Formation to terraforming Mars: The JIMES Expedition to Santorini: *Geomicrobiology Jour.* (online), v. 33 (7): 1-16, 2015.

Service, E., A *Profile of Primitive Culture*, Harper and Row, 1958.

Service, E., *Profiles in Ethnology*, Harper and Row, 1963.

Soodak, H. and Iberall, A. S. Homeokinetics: A physical science for complex systems. *Science*, 201: 579, 1978.

Young, J.Z. *An Introduction to the Study of Man*. NY: Oxford University Press, 1971.

APPENDIX

Homeokinetics:
A Physical Science for Complex Systems

by H. Soodak and A. Iberall[21]

(Appeared in *Science*, 18 August, 1978, Volume 201, Number 4356, pp. 579-582. Reprinted with permission.)

Summary. A physical basis for reductionism is put forth in the form of five propositions that bridge levels of organization in natural phenomena. The outlook is that complex systems and processes all have to be traced back to physical law, which applies the only general scientific constraint on reality, but that out of physical law a hierarchy of organization

---

[21]Dr. Soodak is professor of physics at The City University of New York 10011, and Dr. Iberall is chief scientist at General Technical Services, Inc., Upper Darby, Pennsylvania, 19082

emerges. The basic extension of normal physics in this homeokinetic field form is to complex systems. In such systems the repetitive units of concern are internally complex and exhibit elaborate internal time-delayed processes, for example, memory.

Complex systems do not act chaotically. Instead they exhibit well-defined chains of behavior that have been regarded as purposeful, even historical and evolutionary. Everyday language affords many common descriptive usages which mix up teleological purpose with the physical actions that systems must perform in order to survive. The question can therefore be raised whether there is a common science for the behavior of complex systems, a science that includes the internal control of those essential actions. Simple physical field systems can be defined by statistical mechanics *(1, 2)*. They are ensembles of interacting similar atomic-like particles (atomisms) in which the atomisms equipartition their interactional energy among their mobile internal degrees of freedom. Fluid mechanical fields and solid-state physical fields are examples of such "simple" systems. By extension, complex field systems are those ensembles in which the atomisms have many internal degrees of freedom, and they do not equipartition collisional or interactional energy over each collision cycle, but instead internally time delay, process, and transform such collision energy. They exhibit considerable diversity in their internal activities. Examples of increasing complexity are plastic-elastic behavior, thixotropic behavior (behavior that depends on past history), behavior in living organisms with a more extensive memory system, on up to human societies with an extensive epigenetic heritage as well as an internal (emic) construct for culture.

A Physical Foundation for Complex Systems

We offer some common hierarchical propositions about complex systems found in nature. Together with our proposed basic doctrine of the operation of complex systems, they provide a unified point of view for the scientific study of nature.

While we are aware of many themes regarding the operation of complex systems as they have recently been discussed *(3)*, we are more inclined toward the comment of Anderson *(4)*, who expresses little doubt that physical scientists are reductionists, but points out that the problem is to determine the "constructionist" path with some adequate physical detail.

To establish a physical foundation for complex systems, we take our theme from the originators of homeostasis, Bernard *(5)* and Cannon *(6)*.

Homeostasis. This is the regulation of the internal degrees of freedom of a complex autonomous system, independent of variations or fluctuations in the external milieu. The implication is that such regulation persists for a long time, the lifetime of a system.

Homeokinetics[22]. This is the achievement of homeostasis by means of a dynamic regulation

---

scheme whereby the mean states of the internal variables are attained by the physical action of thermodynamic engines.

The internal state of the complex system (for example, organism) is characterized by the fluxes and potentials that drive and are driven by the engines in a cyclic manner akin to limit cycle behavior. Included as an essential part of this homeokinetic regulation scheme is an ensemble of active catalytic switches, themselves comprising thermodynamic engine parts, which by inhibition or release from inhibition shift the operating points of the engine cycles. As a result, the internal state space is mapped by a ring of operational modes which control the activity of the complex system (7, 8).

L. J. Henderson's 1926 preface to Claude Bernard's seminal work (5) points out that Bernard's principle of the constancy of the internal environment (that is, homeostatic regulation, which may be both cyclic and adaptive) as the condition of free and independent life, is the first approximation to a theory of the organism. We offer the new physical doctrine of homeokinetics as a second approximation to such a theory of complex autonomous systems. Homeokinetics is a technical doctrine of how homeostatic regulation can, in fact, be achieved by thermodynamic engines within physical laws.

These ideas apply not only to the regulation of the internal milieu of the biological system, but also to the invisible regulatory hand of the marketplace in society, as well as to the notion that the observed properties of visible bodies apparently at rest are due to the action of invisible molecules in rapid motion,

Appendix

and the sustained minute motion of larger sized particles embedded among such invisible molecules *(9)*.

A "homeokinetic physics" for complex systems is not independent of the standard physics of elementary processes or simple systems. It clearly must subsume this physics. But in addition, it provides an organizing view for describing, analyzing, and applying physics to all complex viable systems.

In standard physics. the collisional interactions of point-like atomisms can be treated by Maxwell's kinetic theory of gases and its extensions. The averaging techniques of statistical mechanics can be used to derive laws for the motion of ensembles of such atomisms, leading for example to hydrodynamics as a continuum theory for mobile mass particles. Underlying atomicity is identified and used within the dualistic system of atomism and continuum. The atomistic character is first described by kinetics, and the summation of such processes is used to characterize the deviator transport states from equilibrium to establish the continuum description. Independent atomistic particles and idiosyncratic processes are treated by kinetics.

In the case of nonpoint-like atomisms, statistical mechanics describes the internal structure and process within the atomism by a conservative Hamiltonian, resulting in equipartition of energy among the translational and mobile internal degrees of freedom. Such a description is frequently modeled by regarding the atomism as consisting of a set of nondissipative oscillators and rotators.

But this standard approach is inadequate to deal with complex field systems. As we stated, they are ensembles of interacting like atomisms in which the atomisms have many internal degrees of freedom. Such complex atomisms do not equipartition interaction energy per collisional cycle, but instead internally time delay, process, and transform collisional inputs, generally using many fluidlike dissipative mobile steps. We may regard such atomisms as factories, undergoing their process chains. Each atomism, as a factory system, operates homeokinetically. It rings through its operational modes. The process chains furnish their own intrinsic timing, and this factory clock. the internal "day" of the factory, ultimately must be in time with the collisional cycles so as to balance inputs and outputs and maintain homeostatic persistence.

In contrast to the conservative Hamiltonian approach, the homeokinetic view regards the internally complex atomistic factory itself as a field, requiring for its description of the same dual-analysis process—continuum thermodynamics with bordering kinetics. Thereby a natural hierarchy is established as one goes up or down through the size or order of structures. At every level. the complex atomistic entities are internally mobile factories. The cascade complexity of the eddy structure in the turbulent hydrodynamic field provides a physical example.

Complex atomisms do not change their fundamental physical nature on account of their factory complexity. Regardless of hierarchical level, the variables are still mass species, charge, energy, momentum, or action, and they include population number for atomistic species that live and die (with added conservations at more primitive levels). The fundamental spatial field processes remain diffusion, convection, and wave propagation. The complexions are still associations of the one, the few, and the many. The generalized subject "chemistry" is still concerned with the making, breaking, and exchanging of bonds. The internal modal states of the atomisms do not consist of hard-wired. hard-geared (holonomic), hard-molded subcomponents *(10)*. They are alternative paths of nearly equienergetic states, with the pistons; cylinders, valves, and switches of the engine factory arising from the internal hydrodynamic processes. Their component states are more often gel-like than solid. This is the picture we would like to present. To fix the picture, we offer a set of five propositions that illuminate the underlying physics. More detailed discussion of their content may be found elsewhere *(11)*.

Five Propositions

The complex systems in nature may be hierarchically linked by five thermodynamic propositions. A scientific scaffold is thus established that provides conceptual linkages across a great variety of levels of organization from elementary particles below to cosmology above. The level bridging propositions that follow *(12)* thereby provide a "hunting license" to extend the methods of physical science to many kinds of complex systems found in nature.

1) Ensemble mechanics implies thermodynamics. A deterministic continuum description of

homogeneous matter must include dissipation for consistency. In this sense, mechanics implies thermodynamics.

2) Atomistic ensemble below implies continuum above. An ensemble of interacting atomistic entities (atomisms) at any organizational level acts like a continuum at an appropriate space-time scale (for example, a glass of water).

3) Continuum below implies superatomisms above. A fluidlike continuum at any organizational level becomes dynamically unstable locally at some sufficient scale of stress, creating a spectrum of patterned structures of superatomisms that are freely mobile in broadly extended media (for example, small eddies in a turbulent stream).

4) Atomisms below imply superatomisms directly above. The physics of interacting superatomisms, including their internal processes, appears as ad hoc at their level, even though derivable in principle from the physics of the lower atomistic level. However, the Liouville theorem and the existence of a distribution function for the translational degrees of freedom in an ensemble of these superatoms is directly transferred from the lower level (for example, Brownian particles).

5) Continuum above implies fluctuations — generally atomistic — below. The dissipative nature of a continuum, as required by proposition 1, implies fluctuations at a lower level of organization.

These propositions link the hierarchical systems found in nature and imply a statistical mechanics — irreversible thermodynamics — for each level. Earlier presented only as a conjecture (13), the physical

Appendix

framework for natural systems was represented by the notion that these natural systems were organized into successive levels of atomisms (A) and continua (C). An ensemble of atomisms forms a continuum. The continuum becomes dynamically unstable and forms superatoms. The line ... -A-C-A ... ends when it becomes singular at either end, for example, one universe above, fundamental particles (quarks?), below.

In the following paragraphs we briefly outline or exemplify the thrust of each proposition.

Proposition 1. A Newtonian conservative mechanical description of a continuous homogeneous fluid is necessarily incomplete, except for the case of a Hooke's law medium *(14)*, one in which the pressure *p* is a linear function of specific volume *v*. The nonlinear dissipation-free wave equation for such a homogeneous continuum leads to singularities that are described by discontinuities, or shocks. Further, mass, momentum, and mechanical energy cannot all be conserved across a shock front. Mechanical energy here is the sum of kinetic energy and elastic potential energy $e(v) = -\int p(v)dv$. In a "normal shock," mechanical energy is lost. In an "antishock," it is gained. Finally, solutions generally become nonunique when initially smooth solutions generate colliding shocks.

The minimal extension of Newtonian mechanics required to save energy conservation introduces a new nonmechanical parameter, *s,* on which the energy depends. The "missing energy" is then the change in energy due to the change in *s* across a shock, according to $\int(\partial e/\partial s)ds = \overline{T}\,\Delta s$ where T is defined as the derivative $\partial e(v,s)/\partial s$. The missing energy is positive in normal shocks and negative in antishocks. To save Newtonian determinism, to avoid non-uniqueness, it is necessary to disallow antishocks.

Thus, energy conservation demands the introduction of entropy s and temperature T, and determinism demands the positivity of $T\Delta s$ and of dissipation.

Proposition 2. The continuum description of a collection of like atomisms is a standard reduction in the physics of matter *(1)*, in the case that the atomisms easily equipartition energy during collisions. For example, with mobile atomisms, fluids, one obtains the Navier-Stokes formulation valid for space-time scales several times larger than the scales of a molecular collision. An analogous description exists in the solid-state case *(15)*. But as the atomisms increasingly delay collisional energy internally (being out of phase, it is dissipative), the "instantaneous" summation of processes involving translational motion (for example, momentum) and transport (shear viscosity, heat conductivity) are inadequate for the description. Instead, a longer period of integration has to be specified, one long enough for internal degrees of freedom to achieve a total net cycle of balance. That such a cycle must exist, if the system is known to exhibit near stationary dynamic behavior or some weak form of the ergodic hypothesis in finite time *(16)*, is obvious because the materials and energies for the internal degrees of freedom must come through the translational gate. The appropriate measure of the process is λ/η, the ratio of bulk to shear viscosity, and the physical process proposed (as a substitute for momentum balance) is action balance by characteristic internal modes (factory modes), and the ensemble physics is denoted as homeokinetic. As shown by Tisza *(17)*, the ratio λ/η basically measures the ratio of the action involved in the cycle of internal processes to the action appearing in the fluctuating translation processes.

Proposition 3. But now we may imagine a uniform continuum field stretching indefinitely (for example, to remote boundary conditions). The question is, if that system is stressed sufficiently for a given size (or for a given stress, if the size is sufficiently large), can there be a homogeneous time-independent solution? The proposition indicates that at sufficient scale, the same concept as the critical Reynolds number of a transition to some form of inhomogeneity will apply. The generalized concept of the Reynolds number will be that of the ratio of a flux sweeping convectively (nonlinearly) into a local medium, as compared to what local bonding mechanisms can absorb (within its internal thermostatic energy). If this ratio reaches or exceeds one, new local forms have to emerge.

Beyond its obvious validity and exhaustive testing in second-order transition flow phenomena, we show how it may be applied homeokinetically to first order transition condensation or phase change phenomena, including its implications for human transition from hunter-gatherer to settled trading agriculturalist societies.

The basic proviso must be added that for a free and autonomous life, the newly emergent inhomogeneous dynamical element (superatomism) should be small compared to the spatial constraints of the boundaries. Dynamical elements may emerge at first which remain highly confined by the boundaries, but there will exist a sequence of such instabilities, tending toward increasing chaos and smaller size which ultimately will be free.

Proposition 4. If we start at the level of some very small-sized atomism (for example, quark, electron) then there exist ensembles which obey well-known statistical mechanical constraints, for example, a Liouville theorem regarding the conservation of density-in-phase. At this point, we can transfer attention to higher ordered atomisms, if they exist, without concerning ourselves with the intermediate continuum-like state from which the higher ordered superatomistic associations arose. We simply note that in the phase space in which we were watching the original particles, we could find some indefinitely long temporal correlations, the higher ordered superatomisms, Thus there exists a phase space in lower order dimensions for which the same Liouville theorem and a similar translational momentum (or action) description goes through. However, one will have to add, ad hoc, a quantization theory, among hidden variables as it were, by which the atomistic associations occurred. Any new continuum mechanics based on these superatomisms will have to be limited by this higher ordered quantization.

Proposition 5. Proposition 1 demonstrates the existence in a fluid continuum of an energy component that is not macroscopically mechanical, that cannot be accounted for as the sum of macroscopic kinetic and elastic energies. Insistence on a mechanical accounting of energy then implies the existence of lower level motions "fluctuations," with zero mean value.

The scale of such fluctuations can be described only by going beyond the minimal extension of Newtonian mechanics described in proposition 1, and including in the equations smoothing terms which prevent the formation of mathematical discontinuities. The simplest smoothing term from the mathematical point of view is that which corresponds to viscous drag. Inclusion of a viscous term with viscosity η automatically introduces a spatial scale $\eta/(\rho c)$, where ρ is density and c is sonic speed, and an associated temporal scale $\eta/(\rho c^2)$. In a gas, these are the mean free path and collision interval.

Conclusions

A physical reductionist construct has been offered. Its outlook is that complex systems and processes all ultimately have to be traced back to physical law, which applies the only general scientific constraints on reality; but that out of physical law a hierarchy of organization emerges, and that it behooves the generalist or user of general principles to become familiar in a constructive sense, both theoretically and experimentally, with the detailed content of any level that these principles are to be applied to (4).

We realize that the notion that physics is capable of dealing with complex systems such as nature, life, society, mind, has been philosophically offensive to most students in these fields; and that to make such a claim has been offensive to physicists as well. But we are trying to establish the point that simple conservative Hamiltonians for the description of the processes within the atomisms of complex systems are inadequate "constructionist" bases for achieving the task. We ask (i) that serious attention be paid to the internal "hydrodynamic" factory complexity within the atomism (cell, brain, organism, society) *(18)* and (ii) that the cascade complexity of the turbulent hydrodynamic field, such as the atmosphere, be used as a prototype model exercise.

As an organizing view for the analysis of viable complex systems, we present the new physical doctrine of homeokinetics, a dynamic regulation scheme whereby homeostatic persistence is maintained by the action of chains of thermodynamic engine processes. The homeokinetic view of a complex atomism itself as a factory field establishes a natural hierarchy of organizational levels. The basic physics underlying this description is illuminated by five level-bridging propositions.

References and Notes

1. J. Hirschfelder, C. Curtiss. R. Bird, *Molecular Theory of Gases and liquids* (Wiley, New York, 1964).
2. E. Moelwyn-Hughes, *Physical Chemistry* (Macmillan, New York, 1961).
3. L. Jeffress. Ed., *Cerebral Mechanism and Behavior, The Hixon Symposium* (Wiley, New York, 1951); H. von Foerster, M. Mead, H. Teuber, Eds., *Transactions of Conference on Cybernetics* (Josiah

Macy, Jr. Foundation, New York, 1949-1957, vols. 1-5; A. Rosenblueth and N. Wiener, *Philosophy of Science* 10.18 (1943); R. Taylor. *ibid.* 17. 310 (1950); A. Rosenblueth and N. Wiener, *ibid.*, p. 318; R. Taylor, *ibid.*, p. 327; N. Wiener, *Cybernetics* (MIT Press, Cambridge, Mass., 1961); W. McCulloch, *Embodiments of Mind* (MIT Press, Cambridge, Mass., 1961); J. von Neumann, *The Computer and the Brain* (Yale Univ. Press, New Haven, Conn., 1958); F. Ayala and Th. Dobzhansky, Eds., *Studies in the Philosophy of Biology* (Univ. of California Press, Berkeley, 1975); W. Ashby. *An Introduction to Cybernetics* (Wiley, New York, 1956); T. Winograd, paper presented on 29 January 1975 at the Annual Meeting of the AAAS, New York. K. Popper and J. Eccles, *The Self and Its Brain* (Springer-Verlag, New York, 1977).

4. P. W. Anderson, *Science* 177, 393 (1972).

5. C. Bernard, *An Introduction to the Study of Experimental Medicine* (Schuman, New York, 1949).

6. W. Cannon, *The Wisdom of the Body* (Norton, New York, 1939).

7. A. Iberall and S. Cardon, "Further study of the dynamic system response of some internal human systems," NASA CR-219 (National Technical Information Service, Springfield, Va., May 1965). .

8. A. lberall and W. McCulloch, *Journal Basic Engineering,* 91, 290 (1969).

9. We note that the priority of discovery might be considered to be Lucretius. Adam Smith's "invisible hand," Bernard's constancy of the interior, and lastly Maxwell's maintenance of the motion distribution in an ensemble of colliding

molecules. However, it was Maxwell, and later, Einstein in the theory of Brownian motion, who provided a reductionist model for such phenomena.

10. The Enlightenment pursued the notion of Newtonian and Cartesian clockworks which proved inadequate for the complexity of historical and evolutionary processes. An extreme current form of Cartesian clockworks is the circadian rhythm, an expectation among some that it will prove to be *the* timekeeper for biological processes and complex organisms. [See G. Luce, *Biological Rhythms in Human and Animal Physiology* (Dover, New York, 1971)].

11. A. Iberall and H. Soodak. *Collective Phenomena*. 3 (1978).

12. While largely described in a classical spirit, these propositions are essentially neutral with regard to quantum effects.

13. A. Iberall, *Toward a General Science of Viable Systems* (McGraw-Hill, New York, 1972).

14. The motion of a Hooke's law medium is the superposition of noninteracting harmonic acoustic waves. The Hamiltonian separates into a sum of oscillator terms, one for each mode. This is the continuum equivalent of the particle picture situation of a set of noninteracting particles. In both cases, there can be much motion, but nothing can be said to happen. Each particle or each acoustic mode performs its own inertial motion independent of all òthers. Structure and process do not arise without interactions. Nonlinearity is required.

Appendix

15. J. M. Ziman, *Principles of the Theory of Solids* (Cambridge Univ. Press, London, 1965); M. A. Nusimcvici, Ed., *International Conference on Phonons, University of Rennes, 1971* (Flammarion, Paris, 1971).
16. Otherwise it would not be perceived as a system. Note that such conditions have even been satisfied for Earth geologic time, known or surmised since Lyell, and increasingly so even for stellar and galactic time.
17. K. Herzfeld and T. Litovitz, *Absorption and Dispersion of Ultrasonic Waves* (Academic Press, New York, 1959).
18. A. Iberall, *Journal Basic Engineering:* 82, 96 (1960); *ibid.,* p. 103; *ibid.,* p. 513; *Journal of Dynamic Systems, Measurement, and Control* 95, 291 (1973); *Gen. Systems* 18, 161 (1973); ____, H. Soodak, C. Arensberg, "Social Physics, a New Discipline," First International Conference in Biomechanics, Ahem, August 1978; A. Iberall and S. Cardon, *Systems Models for Transportation Problems* (Department of Transportation Report No. D.O.T. TSC-OST-76-12; available from National Technical Information Service, Springfield. Va., 1976), parts 1 to 4.

INDEX

Index

Index

Index

Harry Soodak (1920-2008)

Harry Soodak worked at the Manhattan Project at Oak Ridge National Laboratory where he gave courses in nuclear physics and reactor theory. In 1945 Harry Soodak and Eugene Wigner published the first design of a sodium-cooled breeder reactor. In 1949, Soodak joined the Physics Department of his alma mater, CCNY, where he was widely admired for the brilliance and depth of his understanding of the worlds of physics and mathematics, receiving an Outstanding Teacher Award in 1987. He retired in 1992. Soodak and Iberall had a close connection, having met in college at CCNY. They talked together, sometimes on a daily basis, developing the principles of homeokinetics.

ABOUT THE AUTHOR

 Arthur Saul Iberall (1918-2002) was a Fellow of the American Society of Mechanical Engineers, a Distinguished Lecturer at the Biomedical Engineering Society, and a member of the NY Academy of Sciences. He received an honorary Doctor of Science from Ohio State in recognition of his achievements in interdisciplinary scientific research. Iberall was a consultant to NASA, Dept of Transportation, Army Research Office, the Navy, the Air Force, and chief physicist at Rand Development Corporation and General Technical Systems. His applied work contributed to the development of the first space suit, the high speed dental drill, breathing regulators, fiberglass cutters, and major home appliances such as stove surface burners, the electric knife, and fancy-stitch sewing machines. His NASA Exobiology Program research into the dynamics of mammalian physiological processes led to the development of homeokinetics. He taught courses at UCLA Crump Institute in complex systems. Dr. Iberall published over 200 papers and authored books including *Foundations for Social and Biological Evolution* (1993, Cri-de-Coeur Press) and *Toward A General Science Of Viable Systems* (1972, McGraw-Hill).

Lightning Source UK Ltd.
Milton Keynes UK
UKOW06f1858300817

308280UK00008B/289/P